WRONG BODY, WRONG LIFE

Living with Gender Identity Disorder In Ireland

Sara-Jane Cromwell

MetaCom Publishing

Dedication

*This book is dedicated to the years of my lost life
and to all those who never had the chance to live
and be their true selves.*

MetaCom Publishing
Rockgrove
Midleton
Co Cork

**METACOM
PUBLISHING**

© Sara-Jane Cromwell
ISBN: 978-0-9564763-0-2

Page Layout: Michelle Higgins, Litho Press
Cover Design: Becky Grice
Printed and Bound in Ireland by:
Litho Press, Midleton, Co. Cork.
Tel: 021 4631401

PRINt
IRISH
CLÓBHUAILt
IN ÉIRINN

A CIF catalogue record for this book is available from the British Library.

TABLE OF CONTENTS

ACKNOWLEDGMENTS

This book could not have been written without the encouragement I received from so many people, following the publication of my first book "Becoming Myself", which was published in February 2008.

It has been especially gratifying to have had the support and encouragement from people whom I hold in the highest esteem. Amongst these are Alison Walsh, Rachel Pierce, Niall Crowley and Faith O'Grady, all of whom read the manuscript or parts thereof and whose feedback was invaluable.

Others who stand out over the past number of years are my dear friends Carmel Shortiss, Conny Ovesen, Maria Broderick, Sinead Murphy, Geraldine & Jim Donnelly and Caroline Drake. They all listened patiently and supportively as I waffled on about this book and the unending problems being experienced by people with GID. The lunches and coffees we shared did so much to encourage me. They could never know just how much their encouragements have sustained me while working on this project. They'll be pleased to know that my days of living and working like a hermit have finally come to an end.

Acknowledgement should be given to those NGO's who have steadfastly represented the rights of people with GID and in particular have campaigned for their legal recognition through the introduction of legislation that will give legal recognition to Gender Identity Disorder and the right of these individuals to have their Birth Certificates re-issued with their correct gender. Amongst these organisations are the Free Legal Aid Centre (FLAC), the Irish Council of Civil Liberties (ICCL) and the Irish Human Rights Commission (IHRC). Particular mention should be made of the Equality Authority for their invaluable work on behalf of people with GID and whose input has been immense. Without them, the first medical symposium on GID to be held in Ireland could not have taken place. In this regard I also wish to acknowledge The HSE and the Department of Health and Children who along with the Equality Authority jointly sponsored this historical event.

Mention must be made of the kindness and support of Becky Grice at the East Cork Journal who very generously designed the cover of the book. Also worthy of mention is Wan Waterman and Michelle Higgins at Carrig Print for their professionalism, courtesy and commitment which has helped to make this book what it is.

A special mention should be made of my colleagues on GIDI's Board of Management; they are Catherine Kelly, Sarah Duffy and Dr. Nicholas Krievenko, whose steadfast support over the past two years has been immense and has enabled me to take the time I needed to complete this work.

An acknowledgement should be given to my former colleague Lynda Sheridan. Because, despite our differences, it is fair to say that Lynda has been exceptional in her commitment to the cause of raising awareness about Gender Identity Disorder, and she is to be applauded for her efforts.

I am immensely grateful to Eileen O'Neill, Vincent O'Leary and Ronnie Dorney of the HSE, who were extremely supportive of me during the very difficult events of 2006/07 and who encouraged me to keep going when I was ready to give up. The completion of this book is due in no small way to the encouragement they all gave to me, when I was at such a low point.

If I have neglected to mention anyone here then I am most heartily sorry, but you are certainly acknowledged in spirit.

My heartfelt thanks to you all.

PREFACE

The great danger for most of us is not that our aim is too high and we miss it, but that it is too low and we reach it.
Michelangelo

This book has been nearly six years in the making and follows my own diagnosis of Gender Identity Disorder (GID), which I received in August 2003. It comes after years of researching the condition in terms of its nature and cause, and trying to separate the facts from so much of the nonsense that has been written about it. I will no doubt be accused of being highly selective in the references I have chosen to demonstrate the facts of this condition. But isn't that precisely the point? It is absolutely essential to sift through the voluminous amounts of information (most of it utter rubbish) in order to get to the clinical evidence? Evidence that many would prefer remained hidden.

The amount of misinformation about Gender Identity Disorder is truly staggering. And it can hardly be a surprise then that this misinformation causes so much confusion and harm. If there is one thing that has stood out more than any other during all the years of research, it has been the wilful and stubborn refusal of some to accept the evidence in front of them, because it is at variance with their long held and deeply cherished views on gender and sex. And this has not been helped by those with the condition who refuse to accept the need for a more definitive explanation of what Gender Identity Disorder is, what causes it, and how best to treat it.

I am aware, that publishing this book will be controversial and there are those who will take exception to some of its contents, as it will not agree with their own cherished views on gender identity in general and Gender Identity Disorder in particular. Some may even take offence to some of the more concrete terms and statements used within these pages. This book is inevitably going to annoy some who refer to themselves as *transsexuals* or *transgender*. For example, there are some who clearly do not like the clinical term Gender Identity Disorder and instead prefer something like *Gender Dysphoria*; while others will prefer terms such as *Gender Variance*. There are of course those who prefer to stick with the older and more inappropriate terms such as *Transsexualism* and *Transgenderism*. They do this despite the fact that these terms cause a great deal of confusion with transvestism and crossdressing etc, which are regarded as psychosexual disorders; and only serve to reinforce the very stereotypes that these same individuals say they want to see eliminated. The point should not be lost, even at this early stage, that some of those who take exception to using the term Gender Identity Disorder have their own agendas, some of which are inexplicable and decidedly unhelpful and dangerous. It is time for the confusion to end and this can only be ultimately achieved by adopting a more appropriate terminology for this congenital neurobiological condition.

The overwhelming justification offered for using this inappropriate terminology is because everyone else is using it. This is simply not true. This type of logic is used even by some of those who absolutely agree that the terminology must be changed in favour of Gender Identity Disorder. The 'because everyone else is doing it' argument is really no argument at all. It is merely an excuse not to stand up to those who refuse to do the right thing on this issue. There are many who will disagree with the stance I have taken throughout this book. But as I've recently stated to one of my colleagues: being right is not always easy, nor is it always popular, but it is still right. And in this regard and I am more than happy to allow history to be my judge.

This book needed to be published sooner rather than later due to the ongoing difficulties that people with gender identity problems experience on a daily basis, and also because something definitive needs to be said about the science behind what is a congenital and neurobiological intersex condition. And this is probably the most important point of this entire work: that people are *born* with Gender Identity Disorder. It is *not* a choice they make at some particular point in time in their lives, as is so often assumed by those who know nothing about the condition. The situation is made even more difficult by the very inadequate way in which most people with the condition try to explain it.

There was a time when it was very difficult to clearly define the nature and cause of Gender Identity Disorder, but this is no longer the case, despite the wishes of some to believe otherwise. The evidence is both strong and clear and the treatment paths are well developed, albeit somewhat dramatic in nature and in terms of the implications for those opting for the full or partial Gender Reassignment option.

These issues are particularly important in light of the ongoing legal case currently going through our courts in relation to the right of people with GID to have their Birth Certificates altered so as to reflect their true gender identity, and thereby guarantee them the same right to privacy and equality as afforded to every other citizen within this state. It is hoped that this work will help in clarifying people's thoughts on the medical and legal and social issues involved.

There are few medical or clinical conditions that are as little known and understood as Gender Identity Disorder. The effects of this ignorance have been incalculable on the lives of those born with the condition and indeed for their families.

It is hard for people to imagine just how awful it is to try and live a *normal* life in the wrong body, but I will try to convey it as clearly as I can. All I ask at this point is that you read the following pages with an open mind and that you will be willing to learn something you haven't known before about the great mystery that is *Gender Identity Disorder.*

There have been three significant developments since the completion of this book and which should be included for publication. Firstly, there is the commitment in the new Programme for Government to introduce legislation that will give legal recognition for people with Gender Identity Disorder. Whilst this is of course to be welcomed, it is however regrettable that there is still the use of inappropriate and damaging terminology, with all its negative connotations; and which continues to deter those who genuinely need help from coming forward. This is because they rightly perceive that to do so will be to have their gender identity reduced to a sexual issue rather than a clinical one, which requires the appropriate medical intervention.

Secondly, and very disturbingly, is the call from some groups within the LGBT community, that Gender Identity Disorder be de-pathologised and that people should be free to acquire hormone treatment and Gender Realignment Surgery without any prior diagnosis from a qualified medical consultant. If they confine their call to the de-pathologising of GID as a mental disorder, then there is full agreement (though this is already likely to happen). But there can be absolutely no agreement if they mean (which I have heard from the chair of one of these organisations), the removal of any form of clinical diagnosis before people are prescribed hormones and then to go forward for Genital Realignment Surgery. Their call for de-pathologising GID opens the floodgates for all manner of abuse of medication and surgical procedures, and leaves vulnerable people exposed to serious danger. It also has the effect of disenfranchising the very people they claim to represent. The fact is though they do not represent those who seek appropriate medical diagnosis and treatment for their congenital condition. This call should not be condoned by right thinking people, and the health service authorities and the government are urged to give very careful consideration to this call and those who make it, when drafting appropriate legislation for the legal recognition of Gender Identity Disorder.

Thirdly is, the announcement reported in the Times on December 11th, 2009, which reported the findings of an international team of scientists who identified, the gene that keeps females female. They have discovered that when they artificially switched off the gene in adult female mice their ovaries began to develop into male testes and their testosterone levels were similar to those of healthy male mice. The gene in question is known as FOXL2. What is particularly interesting about this discovery is the gene in question is located on a, *"non-sex chromosome"* (my emphasis). It is believed that this is going to dramatically affect the way in which gender reassignment treatments are carried our in the future. This new evidence regarding the effects of genes and chromosomes on gender and gender identity serves to reinforce the position taken throughout this book, i.e. that Gender Identity Disorder is not a sex or sexual issue, but about one's gender identity.

One of the goals of this book is to save lives that would otherwise be lost through depression, suicide, self-medicating and other extreme measures borne out of people's desperation to resolve their gender identity crisis. Another goal is to save the next and future generations from the hellish existence that is Gender Identity Disorder. If this book helps in contributing towards achieving these goals and helps to open the debate more fully, then the effort will have been worthwhile.

Sara-Jane Cromwell
Cork 2010

INTRODUCTION

What is now proved was only once imagined.

William Blake

Can you imagine it, what it must be like to live in the wrong body as a child; live in the wrong body as a teenager and live in the wrong body as an adult? And can you imagine what it must be like to live in the wrong body but never be able to tell anyone about it nor to be able to explain the reason for it, not even to those who are closest to you? And can you imagine telling those closest to you and those you trust most, when you already know that they are going to blame you for choosing to be like this, making you feel that it's your fault; you tell them knowing full well that they are most likely to ridicule you as a freak, a weirdo and even a pervert? Can you imagine what it's like being a child or teenager, who struggles through school knowing you don't fit in, no matter how hard you try and have to face all the teasing and bullying that children who are different inevitably suffer at the hands of their peers? Or what about when you're an adult who finally plucks up the courage to get medical help for your condition and then proceed to tell your loved ones, friends and work colleagues only to experience more blame, more false accusations, more ridicule, more bullying, and losing your job, family, friends, your world? Can you imagine it? No? Well then, welcome to the world of people with Gender Identity Disorder.

This book is written with the purpose of informing, educating and enlightening people's understanding of a relatively rare but significant medical intersex condition known as **Gender Identity Disorder (GID).** The condition has, until recent times, been more commonly known as **Transgenderism** and **Transsexualism**. It is hoped that by making this information available, people will have a much more accurate understanding of GID and thereby be in a better position to respond in a more considered and compassionate way towards those who live with the condition.

It is extremely important that there is an appropriate and uniform terminology used in reference to Gender Identity Disorder, along with easy to understand definitions and explanations. The anecdotal evidence is overwhelming, in that whenever more appropriate terms and simplified explanations are used, then the responses are much clearer and more supportive than is the otherwise the case. This in turn will give people with GID much greater confidence when making their disclosure. This can also make a significant impact on the overall outcome of the reassignment process.

The book is also written with the aim of placing Gender Identity Disorder where it belongs, within mainstream medicine and social consciousness. This is absolutely vital if we are ever to see a time when those living with this condition can finally come out of the shadows and join mainstream society and be able to come forward and receive the medical and other supports which they so desperately need in order to live their lives normally within their families, communities and workplaces, etc.

By placing this condition in the mainstream it will also be possible to lessen the embarrassment and shame so often expressed by families, friends, work colleagues and communities, which has lent itself to all manner of stigma and discrimination. By addressing the issues more openly and having them discussed more widely, people will very soon realise there is nothing to be afraid of and that they are not dealing with a group of freaks and weirdo's, but rather with very ordinary decent people who just happen to have an extraordinary condition known as Gender Identity Disorder.

This book is not intended to be an exhaustive scientific explanation of GID. This is in part due to the very complex nature of the condition and the difficulty of trying to make that information understandable to a wider public. It is intended therefore to present the scientific data in a manner that can be understood by just about anyone who might be interested in the subject, especially, GP's, counsellors, psychologists, psychotherapists, families, employers etc. The second reason has to do with the ever-growing research into the whole area of gender identity. It aims to bring to light the very real human tragedy that is Gender Identity Disorder and what needs to be done to help those who suffer with the condition. It also aims to assist their families, who must also come to terms with having to get to know, what is effectively, someone they hadn't known before.

The reactions to a disclosure of Gender Identity Disorder can to say the least be very mixed. The worst reactions tend to come from the immediate family, parents, siblings, spouse, children, extended family etc. The person making the disclosure often experiences ridicule, judgementalism and outright rejection, which are the normal reactions when people are confronted with the news or when they *suss* the man dressing as a woman; something they don't understand and see as abnormal behaviour.

Words are rarely, if ever, neutral. This is especially true

when they are used by the media. The media has the power to do great good and great ill by the way in which they present information to the general public and this can have a very deep and lasting impact on the lives of those most directly and indirectly affected by how they report on various stories.

People with GID feel that they should not have to justify their condition, or themselves, but unfortunately they do find they are placed in the awful predicament of having to do so in a society that is simply unable or unwilling to comprehend how they are in the truest sense of the word *victims* of one of nature's cruellest tricks. There is overwhelming evidence that this condition not only exists but that it affects a surprising number of people. The statistics are extremely difficult to nail down, but judging by the anecdotal evidence there are more than originally thought. This could be explained on the basis that as the condition receives better publicity and the health services engage more fully with the clinical aspects of the condition. This gives people greater confidence to come forward and seek the help they need. This then is bound to have a significant bearing on the figures coming forward. The evidence also shows that this condition affects males-to-females and females-to-males alike. By male to female I mean, females born into male bodies and vice-versa. Confusing? Then imagine what it's like living in the wrong body!

The world is a very mean place for people with GID, especially for those who are rejected by those nearest to them. Words like *"devastation"*, *"humiliation"*, *"traumatic"*, *"embarrassment"*, *"shame"*, *"blame"*, *"guilt"*, *"fear"*, *"prejudice"*, *"stigma"*, *"ridicule"*, *"discrimination"*, etc. recur throughout this book, for the simple reason that they are the common everyday feelings and experiences of those born with a congenital intersex condition and Gender Identity Disorder in particular.

Why Wrong Body, Wrong Life?

I chose the title specifically because it has a much better chance of getting people's attention than would have been the case had I used a different and more technical title. In this book therefore, I will be sticking to the terms **Gender Identity Disorder** and **Gender Dysphoria,** in order to emphasise the fact that this condition is about *Gender Identity* and *not* about sexuality or sexual orientation, fetishism, cross-dressing, transvestism, etc. Nor for that matter is it fantasising about being a female and taking drastic steps to become one simply in order to fulfil such fantasies; as claimed by some psychologists and psychiatrists. There is a belief amongst the general public and even amongst people who live with GID that it is all in their own heads, i.e. that it is just in their imagination. This is why so many try to conform to the gender they have been assigned at birth. However, little do they realise just how right they are, but for reasons they could not have imagined. It is no surprise then that people find it hard to come to terms with the fact that the neat simple picture of the male and female gender is anything but straightforward.

This book is born out of my own diagnosis in 2003 and my journey towards full gender reassignment. It is also inspired by my family's response to my disclosure and how typical that response is and is likely to be for many others. It is hoped that by making this information available to the reader, that the treatment recommended by consultants, i.e. *complete gender reassignment* will be better understood and more widely accepted than it is at present.

Chapter One

WHY DO WE NEED TO KNOW ABOUT
GENDER IDENTITY DISORDER?

Facts save lives, even the unpleasant kind

People need to be aware about the true nature of the *clinical* condition known as Gender Identity Disorder or Gender Dysphoria, referred to hereafter as *GID* or *'people with GID'*, and the devastating effects it can have on the lives of those born with it. It can be highly debilitating to a person's daily existence and can lead to a highly dysfunctional life. So much so that there is hardly an area of the person's life that remains unaffected. The effects of this condition can be anything from mild to extremely severe, leading to serious psychological problems, mental illness, alcoholism, drug addiction, self-mutilation and suicide. This is all compounded by the fact that the condition can take a lifetime before it is finally diagnosed, and this is further complicated by society's expectations and the need for people to *fit in*. All of this results in some entering into relationships and commitments they would not otherwise enter into; were they diagnosed and treated much earlier in life. This would help to prevent much of the distress which both they and their families experience.

We need to know this in order that we may respond in the most appropriate and compassionate way possible, thus avoiding any further suffering for those already worn down from their condition. All too often the reactions towards those who reveal themselves as living with GID is to be

1

treated with the utmost disdain, blame and accusations of being selfish, perverts, *dishonest*, mental deviants, and ridiculed to the point of making their lives even more intolerable. All of this is completely unjust and highly destructive. The truth is it does require enormous courage for such individuals to disclose their condition. This is all the more amazing considering that they know in advance the kinds of reactions they can expect, especially when they anticipate the cruel remarks that will be inevitably made towards them. One of the great ironies in trying to be *honest* about the condition is that they are so often accused of being dishonest! It also takes incredible trust to tell anyone about their situation. It is too often the case that all of the best and finest human qualities get trampled over when a disclosure is made. And this includes family, friends, work colleagues, employers, neighbours etc. It is of course not going to be like that with everyone; nonetheless it is all too common an experience for a significant majority. Given the dilemma in which they find themselves, it should be no surprise then that so many choose to hide their condition and opt to conform to their assigned genders, hence the accusation of being *dishonest*. It is the proverbial Catch-22 situation. The question is: how are they to tell their loved one's that they are not what they appear to be? How do they prepare themselves and others before disclosing their condition when so many of them hardly know *why* it is they have the condition in the first place? As with so many other diagnoses, it is often left to each one to discover all the information they can about their condition, which is a major challenge in itself.

One of the effects of all this is the untold horror of some people's desperate attempts to treat themselves in whatever way they can and in some rare cases lead to self-mutilation or to take their own lives through suicide. They choose to do this rather than live with the shame, rejection and isolation that is endemic to this condition. They get the message and so put themselves out of the way. For some the ignominy of a failed suicide attempt compounds their problems. And all of this comes about in so-called civil societies, which pride themselves on being enlightened, tolerant, compassionate and religious. For those who manage to overcome the temptation to attempt suicide the benefits are not always that great. In short therefore, it has to be safe for people to disclose their condition and it must be equally safe for them to seek treatment and to be allowed to live normal lives.

Apart from the obvious and understandable shock at learning that a loved one or friend has been diagnosed with GID, the most common reactions are to be more concerned about how the recipient of the news is likely to be affected; how *they* feel, or what *their neighbours* and *their friends* will think, or, how it will *confuse* or *damage their* children. The person making the disclosure is left reeling from the enormity of what they have done and there is typically no one there with them to offer any kind of support. *Making a disclosure of GID is without doubt one of the loneliest and most difficult things any human being will ever have to do in their lifetime.* Of course families and friends are entitled to feel shocked and families are certainly entitled to their concerns about the ongoing effects on their *own* lives and relationships. However, that simply does not give anyone the right to engage in the kinds of cruelties that are frequently meted out to those who have the courage to disclose their condition. And this is precisely why so many more opt to live with their conflicting gender identities rather than subject themselves to such cruelties. It is sad that those who try to continue hiding their condition are then exposed to the consequences of that decision. This is well demonstrated by the numbers either seriously contemplate suicide or who attempt suicide; rather than to continue subjecting themselves to this kind of situation. This is the extreme end to a deeply distressing life of conflict with one's gender identity, and is probably the single most important reason for learning about Gender Identity Disorder.

Another consequence of society's negative attitudes towards those living with GID is the decision of many of those same individuals to live on the fringes where they feel most safe. And who can blame them. It should be pointed out that this is certainly not their preferred option, but they do feel that they have little or no choice but to hide themselves away. This can also have regrettable consequences.

What's in a Word?

There is a very real problem with the terminology that has been and continues to be used in relation to Gender Identity Disorder. There is still quite a lot of denial on the part of some in regards to the negative associations which surrounds terms such as *Transsexualism* and *Transgenderism*. And for example, that they are frequently associated with other terms such as *transvestism, transmen, transwomen* and *transpeople*. In all the years since I've started my research into GID and my work on behalf of people with GID, I have yet to meet a single person, professional and lay person alike, who does not associate these two terms with sexual fetishist lifestyle choices or some form of sexual compulsion; not one. In fact, I was informed by one of my own consultants that his peers within the field of endocrinology would not engage with the treatment of the condition, precisely because they perceived that these terms referred to the fetish lifestyles mentioned earlier. Hence the need for more clearly defined terms, such as is provided with Gender Identity Disorder and Gender Dysphoria.

So where did these terms come from? The men who first coined and used the terms *Transgenderism* and *Transsexualism* were David Cauldwell and Magnus Hirschfeld respectively. One should not dispute the genuine intentions of these men in inventing these terms, as they had a very specific and appropriate use when they were first used, but at the same time it needs to be acknowledged that the manner in which these terms are currently used continues to be to the detriment of those diagnosed with GID. This has not been helped by the lack of factual information about Gender Identity Disorder as a clinically diagnosable condition. One only has to go to the internet and see the plethora of sites and online e-groups, which openly use these terms in relation to sexual fetishes. Also go to any adult shop and see the number of magazines which use these terms in their titles and advertisements. This is consistent with how most people and organisations understand these two terms and to suggest otherwise is simply preposterous.

Terminology should not be followed slavishly, especially when it adds more confusion and stigma to that which already exists. And this is precisely the situation with *Transgenderism* and *Transsexualism*. They served their purpose at the time but are wholly inappropriate now and for the future. Terminology should be as specific and definitive as possible in relation to the condition it seeks to identify. This is especially true of any terminology used in connection with Gender Identity Disorder.

5

The Role of the Media

These issues are made more difficult by the manner in which the various media treat stories concerning people with GID. For the most part they are salacious, titillating, sleazy and downright inaccurate. But worse still, they give a completely wrong impression of those who struggle on a daily basis to live with their condition and who choose to go through the Gender Reassignment process. The media regularly refers to such people as having a *sex change*. This kind of reporting makes life even more intolerable for those people and their families and only serves to reinforce the public's ignorance and prejudices toward them. It should be acknowledged though, that in recent times certain media have adopted a much more responsible and sensitive approach to the subject and have been a positive force in terms of informing the public about the condition. This will be addressed in more detail later on.

Personal Responsibility

There is an argument to be made about the way people with GID handle their situation and it is true that their own behaviour or approach can often predetermine the reactions and responses they are likely to receive. But for the most part, where a disclosure is to be made, there is a responsibility on loved ones and friends to respond appropriately and sensitively at this critical moment. The experience of most people with GID is that it doesn't make much of a difference how they disclose their condition, even when they do it in the correct manner. The reactions are, for the most part, the same as those outlined above. The truth is that there is no easy way of dealing with this condition in terms of how to disclose it or in how others are likely to react. It is bound to be difficult when hearing a loved one tell them they are in the wrong body, and have therefore been living the wrong life. If we are ever to get to grips with GID and other similar conditions then we must learn as much as we can about the condition itself and how it affects the lives of those it touches directly and indirectly. *We* all pay a terrible price for our ignorance of this and other intersex conditions. But it doesn't have to be like this. There is a far better and more humane approach to dealing with this condition. And by knowing all there is to know, *we* can find that *way* and make life so much better for all concerned. This is another important reason why *we* need to know about GID.

In summary then it can be said, that by knowing more about the true nature of Gender Identity Disorder, we are in a much better position to make the most appropriate response to those disclosing the condition. And in doing so we also make it safe for others to come forward and seek the necessary medical interventions. We also reduce the possibility of people being stigmatised and discriminated against, which would otherwise force them onto the fringes, which is something they have no wish to do. We need to be aware that people go where they feel most safe. Therefore, if we want people to be honest and open about who and what they are, then we have a moral obligation to exercise greater openness and acceptance of them, regardless of their differences. This means accepting the reality that human nature is both highly complex and varied, and as a result of this complexity we are bound to be different in so many ways; that we are not the same. We are all different, all unique, and we need to stop getting so bent out of shape because of it.

Also, by being more aware of the existence of GID, parents, families etc., will be in a much better position to recognise at least the possibility of the condition at a much earlier age. This will give each child a chance to develop more naturally into their true gender identity, rather than having a gender indicated by external physical indicators forced upon them. This awareness could make it possible for parents to seek early diagnosis and ensure the child develops in a way that is more natural and appropriate for them. This will also make it a great deal easier to transition at the appropriate age. By taking this approach we will be ensuring a legacy that future generations will never have to go through the awful difficulties, traumas, prejudices etc. that this and previous generations have had to endure; just because they had the misfortune to be born with GID.

Chapter Two
WHAT IS GENDER IDENTITY DISORDER?

Natura enim non imperator, nisi parendo. Nature cannot be ordered about, except by obeying her.
Bacon, Novum Organum, 1620

To quote from the Irish Medical Journal: *Gender Identity Disorder is a relatively rare condition of atypical gender development in which there is a psychological perception of the self as masculine or feminine which is incongruent (inconsistent) with ones phenotype (physical appearance)[1].* GID is a *Congenital Intersex* condition in which the person is convinced she/he was born into the wrong body and therefore the wrong sex and gender at birth. It works like this: a child born with male genitalia (sex organs) is typically assigned the male sex and gender identity and therefore raised as a boy, and a child born with female genitalia is typically assigned the female sex and gender identity and is therefore raised as a girl. It couldn't be simpler, right? Well for the most part yes. And for most people this is as simple and absolute as it gets. However, the evidence shows unequivocally that it is not as black and white as it first appears.

In order to get to grips with the nature of GID and its underlying cause/s it will be necessary to look at the condition in the broader context of other intersex conditions It is important to see how the foetus develops during gestation and the effects caused by chromosomal and hormonal anomalies; this we will venture to do in this

9

chapter. It should be stated from the outset that there are no easy answers as to the causes and effects of GID, but there can no longer be any serious doubt about its existence and its effects upon those born with the condition.

What is an Intersex condition?

Under normal circumstances, the sex and gender identity of each person will be consistent across all areas, i.e. the female gender will be matched by a female body and female sex / reproductive organs and for males it will be with male bodies and male sex / reproductive organs. This means that in all aspects of gender and sex females will be entirely consistent with the **XX** chromosomes, while males will be entirely consistent with the **XY** chromosomes. But as with so many other things in life, nature is her own mistress and follows to her rules rather than in strict accordance with the norms we demand or expect from her. Nature sometimes causes things to work out differently than we expect or even desire and in such ways that we have no control whatsoever. This is certainly the case with intersex conditions such as GID.

It is the **Y** chromosome that determines whether a foetus is to develop as a male and it is this chromosome that causes the production of male hormones, thus establishing the male sex and gender as distinct from the female sex and gender. This means that during a normal gestation period, the brain, organs, genitalia etc., develop consistently as male, or, female in the case of the Y chromosome. This of course means that each foetus in the womb is highly dependent upon its sensitivity to certain hormones. These hormones also affect the development of the brain, which will ultimately identify itself as either male or female. This means that a normally developed foetus with consistent **XY** chromosomes and who has consistent hormonal sensitivity will go on to develop consistent masculine brain development and go on to identify throughout life as a male, while the foetus with consistent **XX** chromosomes will go on to develop and identify throughout life as a female. This is the expected norm and for the most part this is exactly how it works. However it is not always this straightforward.

Again it must be emphasised that when this works consistently then the male will develop consistently as expected. The same is true of females whose sex and gender depends upon the **XX** chromosomes. But with GID as with other intersex conditions, these rules simply do not apply. Something goes wrong and causes the foetus to develop in ways that can be significantly different from the normal development we would expect during the gestation period. Every foetus is dependent upon the consistent availability of the right hormones which affects the development of the brain and in such a way as is consistent with the development of the foetus' sex development, i.e. sex organs (genitalia). Where there is inconsistency, there is also the potential for GID and other intersex conditions to occur. The following diagram illustrates the female and male chromosomes, in the case of Turners Syndrome.

Diagram 1: Female and Male Chromosomes[2]:

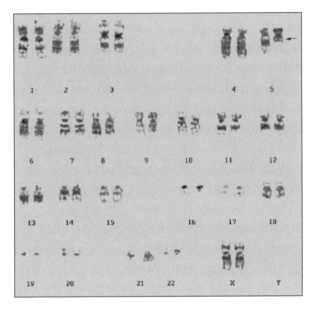

The vast majority of people never have to question their gender or sex and are generally oblivious to the notion that there could ever be a reason to do so. This is because the vast majority of us judge by the physical appearance of each child and especially by their sex organs and it is on this basis that we assign each child its social gender role; the one we all must live with and conform to throughout our lives. It is the gender role we are conditioned to and expected never to deviate from; hence the gender identities stated on our birth certificates. On the face of it this seems entirely reasonable. The problem is that this is not true of all males and all females. This is because gender and sex are far more complex than we realise and is demonstrated by the variety of anomalies that can occur within the chromosomes of each foetus during gestation along with their effects upon hormonal distribution and the subsequent development of the foetus. This has a significant influence on the gender identity of each child and the gender they identify with as they mature into adolescence and adulthood. These anomalies are well known and well documented, and we will look at some of them here, along with the effects they can have in the lives of those born with an intersex condition. And make no mistake about it; the effects can be truly devastating!

Whilst it is true that scientists cannot determine some of the causes for these chromosomal anomalies, there can be no doubting their existence and the impact they can have. As research continues we may be able to more clearly answer the questions regarding these anomalies and just maybe we will find ways of eliminating them or treating them.

There are several possible reasons for the anomalies found in some foetus's during the critical gestation period: (a) it could be that the mother has absorbed hormones from external sources such as medications etc., that are then passed on to the developing foetus during the most sensitive stages of gestation; or (b) it may be that the foetus is insensitive to certain hormones which then affect its development during gestation and beyond. One of the main anomalies we know of is the addition or, absence of the X or Y Chromosomes, e.g. some foetuses have XXY rather than XY, or it could be XYY. Each anomaly produces its own effects on the development of the foetus and subsequently upon the life of the child born with those anomalies. These anomalies will almost always cause the foetus to develop differently to what might otherwise be expected and this could result in very serious risks to the unborn child. For the most part, many of the anomalies and their effects go undetected, until that is, the baby is born. And in some cases, as with GID they may not be detected for many years, if ever! This may result in delayed diagnosis or in no diagnosis at all. A number of the anomalies result in what we now term **Intersex** babies, but were previously known as **hermaphrodites**. The frequency of babies born with anomalies to their *sex/gender differentiation* is as high as 5 per 1,000 (Gooren et al)[3]:

Professor Louis Gooren has stated that:

So far I have described the orderly normal sexual differentiation of becoming a boy or a girl, a man or a woman. It is unfortunate that this process is liable to errors. In about 5 in every 1000 individuals this process has shown some errors. It is also a bit of an admonition to those who always state: so God created man in His own image: male and female created He them. Doctors can testify: in the vast majority of cases with impeccable result, in about 5 in every 1000 individuals there are sex errors. The sexual differentiation has not followed its normal course[4].

To put this in context, it will be worth looking at the following diagram which illustrates the stages through which male and female genitalia develop and what can happen where anomalies exist and how these anomalies could result in baby's being born with incomplete or double genitalia leading to the development of an intersex condition.

Diagram 2: Development of the Male & Female Genitalia[5]:

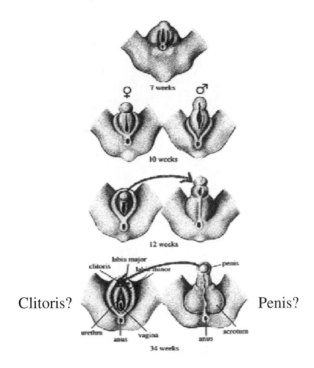

Clitoris?   Penis?

One such condition is known as **Partial Androgen Insensitivity Syndrome (pAIS)**. This condition involves the presence of the **XY** chromosomes, which should typically result in the foetus developing as a normal male with the accompanying male genitalia, rather than female genitalia. Male genitalia are dependent upon the presence of the Androgen hormone. Where there is insensitivity to this hormone the foetus may develop with the genitalia of both male and female sexes with various degrees of development in both genitalia.

Diagram 3: Baby born with Congenital Adrenal Hyperplasia (CAH)[6].

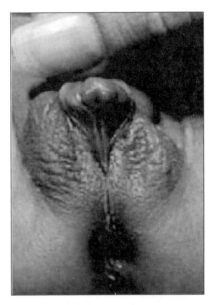

A second example of AIS is that of **Complete Androgen Insensitivity Syndrome (cAIS)**. This involves babies being born with the physical appearance of a female and reared as a female and so the child identifies as a female, but in fact the child is chromosomally male. Some of these children will however identify as male. The problem may not be detected for some years, e.g. around the time when the *girl* is due to start her menstrual cycle, but fails to do so. She is taken for examination and only then is she found to have no uterus and in fact may have male gonads (genitalia) growing internally. The girl in this case is genetically male.

Where there is the existence of both genitalia, some paediatricians have assigned the babies one sex or the other and expected the child to conform to the sex and gender assigned. But it has been too often the case that the child identified with the exact opposite gender to the one assigned them from birth.

What is so extraordinary about these conditions is the fact that members of the medical profession and parent's were prepared to keep the truth of these conditions from their patients, the children; preferring instead to act upon the basis of their own assumptions and embarrassment; though in many cases parent's sincerely believed they were acting in the best interests of their child and would most likely have been acting upon any medical advice they would have received at the time. However it is also fair to say that the parents in these cases are left with a terrible dilemma subsequent to making their earlier decisions. Some children with female features are never told that they are genetically male. Instead they are informed that they simply did not develop wombs like other girls. Some of these children have to wait until they reach adulthood before learning the truth about being genetically male and very often end up devastated at the deception of their parents and doctors. One can only imagine the sense of betrayal they must feel. This is understandably an extremely sensitive and difficult subject for any parent to have to deal with, but this cannot excuse the fact these children's lives are devastated, especially when there is no way back for some of the children affected.

Gender & Intersex Testing in the Olympic Games

If there is any doubt as to the extent of this problem then we need only look at the situation that has prevailed until just recently within the International Olympic Committee in terms of its treatment of female athletes. One of the best or worst kept secrets of the Olympic Games has been the fact, that for 40 years, female athletes have been subjected to the indignity of *gender-testing* to establish if they were *genetically female*. The motive behind these tests was to prevent intersex females from competing, on the basis that *these females* had a competitive advantage over *normal* females. The consequences of this procedure can be both distressing and humiliating for the athletes tested and especially for those found to be biologically male, i.e. to be **cAIS XY** females etc. The humiliation can be made worse in cases where the results were made public and resulted in the athletes being disqualified! This is incredibly inhumane and surely must be a breach of those individual's human right to privacy and human dignity. This is especially difficult for those females who did not identify as males, despite the presence of the **Y** chromosome.

While these *gender tests* were withdrawn in 1999 in time for the Sydney Games of 2000, they were reintroduced for the Beijing Olympics in 2008. There was no such testing for the 2004 Games in Athens and *post-operative females* were permitted to compete, thus ending this appalling and grossly immoral and unethical discrimination against women with an intersex condition. As already pointed out, this situation is due to an extremely narrow definition of both sex and gender identity and a demonstrable ignorance of its underlying causes.

The following excerpt is taken from the Guardian Newspaper of 30th July, 2008: One of the most tragic recent cases is yet to reach a conclusion. Soundarajan, a 27-year-old Indian athlete, has had to endure public humiliation after she was stripped of her silver medal for the 800m at the Asian games in 2006. Soundarajan, who has lived her entire life as a woman, failed a gender test, which usually includes examinations by a gynaecologist, endocrinologist, psychologist and a genetic expert.

This is regrettably typical of the treatment meted out to people with intersex conditions and it needs to be exposed for the abuse that it is.

Intersex conditions have been around for as long as humans have lived on the planet, but it is only in recent decades that any meaningful attempts have been made to get to grips with them. One such effort was that of Johns Hopkins University. They developed the theory that gender is not merely a matter of having XX or XY chromosomes. They opted for the idea that we are gender neutral at birth and that we acquire our gender identity through our developing genitalia and from our environment. The emphasis was therefore on *physical appearance* and environmental influences rather than on the child's genes[7]. One of the most influential theories about why a child failed to conform to their assigned gender was because the child was considered to have been unduly influenced by its environment, e.g. parents etc., or that they were suffering with a mental illness! And this became the basis for treatments designed to bring the person into conformity with their assigned gender. This approach has proven to be quite unsatisfactory and destructive for those suffering from what is now recognised as GID, a congenital rather than a psychiatric or sexual condition.

Another approach developed during the 1960's involved using plastic surgery to correct the (deformed) genitals for boys and girls and assigning their gender accordingly. By changing the male genitals to those of a female they were arbitrarily assigning the child a female gender and vice-versa and the child is then raised in conformity to the assigned gender by the parents. This appears to have been done without any regard for the possibility that the child may not actually identify with the assigned gender. Dr. John Money PHD[8] one of the leading Gender theorists at the time was the principal proponent of this approach, believing that gender was chiefly dependent upon how the child was reared and the way in which it socialised. He was not prepared to allow intersexed babies to develop with both sets of genitalia and therefore insisted on assigning one or the other gender to the baby, insisting that the genitalia and upbringing would suffice in establishing the child's female gender identity. On the face of it this seems like the only viable solution, but as we will see shortly it was an approach that caused far more problems than it solved and with devastating effect.

It is poor science to ignore the most obvious variations which nature produces, just because they don't fit in with our compulsive need to classify everything in absolute terms whether philosophically, religiously, scientifically or legally. The medical profession should be extremely cautious about arbitrarily assigning a particular gender upon children born with both male and female genitalia. To do so is to do a great disservice to the child, and to the child's future. Surely it is preferable to allow each one to develop their gender identity naturally. Allowing each child's gender to develop naturally will be far better than leaving them vulnerable to the tremendous damage, which may result later on.

Most post-natal surgeries carried out on intersex babies are towards the female sex/gender, which was the easier option chosen by surgeons and parents alike, on the assumption that it was in the best interest of the children affected. This is because it is much easier to change small or missing penises in boys to female genitalia. This has since been proven not to be the case. Given that this kind of surgery has been performed in anything up to 1 in 2000 births[9] there has been a considerable number of babies reassigned the wrong gender simply on the basis that their intersex condition was deemed unacceptable.

And it's not as if there were no opponents to this arbitrary approach to gender assignment. Milton Diamond for example was a strong opponent to Money's approach and surgical practices. Using evidence from biology, psychology, psychiatry, anthropology and endocrinology, he was able to show that our gender does not merely derive from our genitalia (nature) and upbringing (nurture). Instead he was able to demonstrate that our gender identity is far more complex than had been assumed up to that point in time. He put forward the idea that our gender identity is imprinted in our brains from *conception!* Unfortunately such revelations were not to be wholly welcome because the old ideas about gender identity and conformity where so deeply ingrained into the minds and attitudes of the *"medical, psychiatric and psychology communities"*. And it was on this basis, i.e. Money's views on gender identity that countless numbers of babies were surgically reassigned over the following decades. The disclosures of the last number of years have revealed some horrendous facts about Money's theories and the effects of his surgical reassignments. Take for example the case of David Reimer. David's case is a tragic and cautionary tale to all those who would force children to live out their lives in a particular gender simply on the basis of their genitalia. And the idea that they can be *conditioned* to live within that assigned gender role, even when there is significant evidence to the contrary, whether physical or behavioural.

David Reimer was born in 1965 and was one of two twins. He was originally named Bruce while his brother was named Brian. After reaching his seventh month, baby Bruce was taken with his twin brother Brian to hospital in order to be circumcised. The circumcision was to be carried out using electrical equipment, which unfortunately malfunctioned and completely destroyed Bruce's penis. The parents were quite understandably shocked and horrified by this and were at a loss as to what to do. Sometime later they were watching television and saw the psychologist and sexologist, Dr. John Money being interviewed about a sex gender clinic he was setting up. Based upon what Bruce's parents had heard they felt that Dr. Money could be the person to help them. They and Dr. Money met up and sure enough Dr. Money told the parents that he could help them to resolve their dilemma.

As it just so happened, Dr. Money had been developing a theory of his own about gender identity and how it develops. He came up with the theory that children are born gender neutral for the first two years and that how they see themselves as male or female depends on their upbringing and how they're nurtured. In order to test his theories Dr. Money needed two small boys and this is where the Reimer twins came in. Bruce's parents were desperate to help their child and Dr. Money gave them what seemed like the best way of doing just that. So it was agreed that Bruce would be brought up as a girl and that he would never be told that he was once a boy. This fact was also kept from his brother Brian. Dr. Money warned Bruce's parents not to tell her that she was a boy, because it would cause the sex change to fail.

Just before Bruce reached two years of age he was castrated and given a rudimentary vulva in order to give him the physical appearance of a girl. This would have been helped along by the fact that Bruce could no longer produce testosterone due to his testicles having been removed. He was then given the name Brenda. And so it was that he started life as a girl and even took on the physical appearance of a girl; except of course that he was still a boy. And for the first few years it actually looked like he was identifying as a girl, much to everyone's relief.

Early interviews with Brenda seemed to indicate that she was in fact identifying quite comfortably as a girl. Believing that his experiment had been a success Dr. Money proceeded to write a book entitled *Man Boy, Woman Girl,* in which he revealed his success to the world. This was in 1972, when Brenda was just seven years old. However all was not as it had seemed and serious problems were developing with Brenda's gender identity. The older she became the more she took on a male identity and male physical features. Brenda was treated very cruelly by boys and girls her age, which saw her as a bit of a freak. Girls would not play with her because she wanted to play with boy's things, and boys wouldn't play with her because she was a girl. She was quite literally in a no win situation not of her making, but for which she was made to pay the price.

Brenda attended a number of interviews with Dr. Money along with her twin brother. Dr. Money tried repeatedly to convince Brenda that she was a girl, but with less and less success. The turning point came after Brenda's last interview with Dr. Money in 1978, when Brenda was just thirteen years old; during which he tried to convince her to have an operation which would give her a new vagina, and that this would confirm for once and for all that she was a girl. It was during this period that Brenda's male features were becoming more pronounced as were her male character traits.

Yet despite the growing evidence to the contrary, Dr. Money persisted in his efforts to convince her otherwise and that she was a girl. The whole experience proved traumatising for Brenda and she became highly suicidal, so much so that she told her parents that she would kill herself rather than meet with Dr. Money again. It was at this point that her parents felt they had no other option but to tell her that she was originally a boy. But while Brenda reacted extremely well to this disclosure, her brother took it rather badly and withdrew from her. Very soon thereafter Brenda began living as a boy and changed her name to David. But by now the damage had been well and truly done. This was to affect David throughout the remainder of his life until his death by suicide in 2004. David's life became increasingly unbearable over time and following a number of personal disasters he went to a car park outside a shopping centre and shot himself. He was just 38 years of age.

There are thousands of David Reimer's the world over who are being made to pay the price for society's neurotic need for fitting everyone into their respective categories and to have them conform to what is most comfortable for society, regardless of the damage it does to the individual.

Only in fairly recent times has any meaningful follow-up been carried out on those people who have been surgically reassigned as females. For example, there were other cases of people with **XY** chromosomes and who were found to have missing penises as babies (Cloacal Exstrophy Syndrome) and were changed from boys to girls and raised as girls. The problem is that those who are surgically changed to females actually identified as males and as such they were effectively mutilated in order to conform to what we now know to be invalid theories regarding gender and sex identity. These follow-ups were conducted only after the Intersex Society of North America (ISNA)[10] brought great pressure to bear on the authorities to investigate the long-term effects of corrective reassignment surgery over the years. All children assigned as girls behaved as boys and wanted to be changed into boys. Some sought to have girlfriends, but of course were unable to do so. None of those who have been reassigned as girls can be reconstructed to conform to their *true* gender identities. Such is the extent of the damage done to these reassigned females that they are unable to enjoy normal sexual relations. What a terrible price to have to pay because of the arrogance and prejudices of those who refuse to move beyond their own favoured theories, regardless of the fact that they are proven invalid or at the very least highly suspect.

As already mentioned, Professor Diamond's work has proven that gender identity is not merely a matter of a person's genitalia and upbringing. He also helped to disprove a long cherished notion amongst the psychiatric profession that those people who suffered with GID were suffering from some form of mental disorder. As we will see shortly, he was absolutely correct.

Another example of an intersex condition is the condition known as Turners Syndrome (see diagram below). This is were a baby is born with the **X** chromosome but with a missing **X** or **Y** chromosome and where the female child appears to have normal female genitalia and reproductive ducts, but incomplete ovaries, and in fact are intermediate male – female. As with so many other intersex children their lives prove to be extremely difficult and torturous.

Diagram 4: The Missing Chromosome in Turner's Syndrome[11]

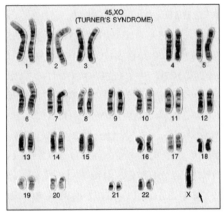

One of the more notable cases is that of Jane Spalding[12] who was wrongly reassigned. She is the founding Director of the Intersex Society of North America. Her aim is to lift the lid on the secrecy and shame that has surrounded the whole issue of intersex conditions and the arbitrary surgical reassignments that have been carried out on untold numbers of infants over a number of decades. It is also to expose the false ideas that being intersex is a matter of shame or that such people are freaks. It is estimated that as many as five children a day are subjected to surgical reassignments (some of which are unnecessary) in America alone, multiply this by the numbers in other countries and the picture becomes clearer as to how many thousands are subjected to this treatment and a lifetime of misery afterwards!

Enough has been said here to show just how complex and varied the issues of gender and sex are, and thereby demonstrating that it is far from being black and white. We are now at a the most fascinating point of dealing with what it is that actually causes each of us to identify with one gender or the other. This brings us right up to date in terms of the evidence that is currently available to the medical professions.

How do we get Our Gender Identity?

It has long been established that our gender identity is located in the brain and definitely not limited to our genitals, reproductive organs or our upbringing. It has been known for quite some time that the Hypothalamus was the region of the brain most closely associated with our gender identity and it is to here that scientists are turning to establish the clearest links to date between gender identity and GID. This research has even brought the John's Hopkins University full-circle with the recognition from the likes of William Reiner, M.D., a paediatric clinician, who states that gender identity must ultimately rest with the child who identifies as one gender or the other, and that researchers must be more willing to listen and learn rather than arbitrarily assign gender on the basis of *sexual function* or *indicators*. He states as follows:

"In the end it is only the children themselves who can and must identify who and what they are. It is for us as clinicians and researchers to listen and to learn. Clinical decisions must ultimately be based not on anatomical predictions, nor on the 'correctness' of sexual function, for this is neither a question of morality nor of social consequence, but on that path most appropriate to the likeliest psychosexual developmental pattern of the child. In other words, the organ that appears to be critical to psychosexual development and adaptation is not the external genitalia, but the brain." [13]

27

Interestingly he also rejected the use of *morality* as a basis for determining a person's gender identity. This is a major step forward in medical thinking and deserves full consideration.

Among the leading eminent experts in GID is the Endocrinologist Dr. Louis Gooren M.D. PHD, Dr. Dick Swaab Professor of Neurobiology and Dr. Frank Kruijver, Researcher, at the Netherlands Brain Institute. Dr. Gooren has treated approx. 3,000 people with GID and is one of the leading experts in this field. The work he and his colleagues have done has been extraordinary and the results of their research can leave even die-hard members of the medical profession and for that matter legislators, in little doubt as to the evidence for GID. For nearly two decades now, Dr. Swaab and his colleagues have studied the brains of deceased GID women and the results have been truly startling. It has been a long held conviction amongst some neurobiologists, psychologists and endocrinologists that the answers to the question of what causes GID lay in the brain and in the Hypothalamus in particular. If this proved to be the case then the reality would be that the brains of GID females are hard-wired in terms of their gender identity and therefore cannot be changed. This would be the best possible confirmation to those diagnosed with the condition, that they are not abnormal, but are in fact behaving very normally. This would certainly have a profound effect on any treatments offered to patients diagnosed with GID.

These and other experts have discovered that gender identity is not fixed on birth. It is in fact established another 3-4 years after birth (Gooren et al)[14]. There are four stages towards gender/sex differentiation:

Stage 1. Establishment of the chromosomal
configuration (**XX or XY**)

Stage 2. Gonadal differentiation
(ovaries or testes)

Stage 3. Differentiation of internal and external
genitalia

Stage 4. Differentiation of the brain into male or
female

As previously stated, the process of brain-sex differentiation takes up to 3-4 years to develop, which means that under normal circumstances this process is straightforward and follows the normal assumptions for sex and gender identity, but not where anomalies occur. So it will take up to four years for the child's actual gender identity to fully form. This will help to explain why children of this age manifest behaviour that is inconsistent with their assigned gender, i.e. girls adopting *tomboy* characteristics, while boys take on more *effeminate* characteristics (sissy's). In most cases these characteristics disappear over time, but for others they persist to the point where they must be suppressed if they are to conform to their assigned social gender roles. In later life, circumstances will conspire to ensure that these gender character traits reappear, thus leading to accusations of deceitfulness when the condition is disclosed. Prof. Gooren has stated that: "Transexualism (GID) strikes where it pleases and you find people of all walks of life in your Transgendered population all over the world."[15] Later we will meet some of these very extraordinary people.

Dr. Dick Swaab et al has demonstrated through the neurobiological evidence from GID male-to-females and biological males and females as to just how distinctive their hypothalamus's are from each other in terms of their neuron patterns. This evidence came about as a result of the detailed research carried out on deceased GID females over the two decades. The Hypothalamus's of heterosexual males, heterosexual females, homosexual males and GID females were sliced by use of a microtome and compared against each other to see what differences, if any, exists between them. The results were truly astounding and confirmed what GID people have always felt, *"that their brains are not like others."* However some have questioned the results saying that the similarities could be explained by these GID females using female hormone treatments. This problem is emphatically answered by the evidence which shows that some of the hypothalamus's examined were of GID females who had *not* undergone any kind of hormone treatment. The diagram below shows the differences between biological male and female hypothalamuses. Note the similarities between the biological female and the GID female hypothalamus's.

Diagram 5. A Comparison of the Hypothalamus's of Males & Females and GID Females:[16]

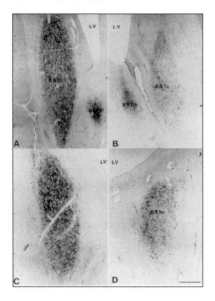

Hypothalamus **A**. belongs to a heterosexual male
Hypothalamus **B**. belongs to a heterosexual female
Hypothalamus **C**. belongs to a homosexual male
Hypothalamus **D**. belongs to a male to female Person GID

It is clear from the diagram on the previous page, that this part of the GID female brain is quite similar to those of biological females, and dissimilar to those of heterosexual or homosexual males. This however does not fully explain why these particular hypothalamuses develop this way, but it shows that they definitely do. By being aware of this we can go a long way towards accepting the facts of this condition. Also it will help our understanding of why it is that counselling and therapy can only have a very limited effect in helping people with GID live with their condition, and why it is that so many opt for gender reassignment instead. This is extremely important in that it gives such a clear understanding of why male-to-female and female-to-male people with GID are living in such states of conflict. We'll look at this in greater detail later on. For now we can say as Dr. Gooren has said, *"it is the body that's the lie!"*[17]

What is its Prevalence?

The numbers affected are estimated to be 1:10,000 – 1:30,000 in male to female and 1:30,000 – 1:120,000 for female to male. However these figures should be treated with the utmost caution as they are subject to change in light of greater awareness of the condition. It is believed with greater awareness the numbers presenting for diagnosis will grow substantially and this in turn will affect the overall figures.

Dispelling the Myths & Stereotypes

It is time to dispel some of the myths that surrounds GID and this can be done by stating the following:

- GID is not a Psycho Sexual condition
- People with GID do not choose their gender identity
- People with GID are not mentally ill
- People with GID are not homosexuals in denial
- People with GID are not freaks
- People with GID are not transvestites/crossdressers
- People with GID are not acting out a sexual fantasy
- People with GID are not shemales

- Marital and family breakdown is not inevitable after a diagnosis of GID

- Gender Identity Disorder cannot be treated or cured through prayer and fasting.

A great deal of distress is experienced by people with GID because of the mistaken association between GID and mental illness. It is especially important to dispel this particular myth by referring to the evidence that GID is in fact a congenital neurobiological condition.

Objections to the Evidence

It is inevitably the case that some will object to the evidence presented here and indeed they have questioned it by stating that the sampling was quite small. In fact the sampling is in excess of a dozen or more at this stage and is a good representative sample on the basis of the results it has produced, which to the dislike of the objectors, is actually quite consistent and some would argue conclusive. But in order for these samples to be obtained the brain must be examined post-mortem, so the sampling will not be that great to begin with. However the objectors don't stop there, they also state that the similarities between the biological female hypothalamus and the GID female's hypothalamus could be explained on the basis of the GID female being treated with female hormones. The evidence quite clearly demonstrates that the sample includes hypothalamuses of GID females who had *not* in fact received hormone treatment.

Some objectors maintain the view that patients diagnosed with the condition should *not* go down the road of gender reassignment, that they should receive therapy instead and that they can be treated in such a way as to *make them comfortable* with their biological gender, i.e. they should just accept that they are males because they have a penis and females because they have a vagina. This is the favoured position of most religious groups including the Roman Catholic Church. They do this on the theory that there is something within these people's environment that caused them to think that they are of the opposite gender, e.g. their mothers and fathers influence, or that they are mentally ill. They hold the view that these variables will explain why some children have a gender conflict. One doctor recently went as far as to make the absurd assertion that it was merely a matter of an *'over belief system'* that one was of the opposite gender. He based his opinion upon the following phrase in the World Health Organization (WHO) International Classification of Diseases-10 description of GID: defines GID as *'a desire to live and be accepted as a member of the opposite sex...'* An unfortunate choice of phrasing should not be allowed to hide the fuller explanation given by the ICD 10, which our friend has conveniently excluded from his quote.

There is a very important point to be made here and it is this: while it is true that there are a number of variables involved in determining our true gender, some of these variables are fixed to the degree that they cannot be altered. The hypothalamus is one such variable. If the hypothalamus, which is where we derive our gender identity, (as distinct from our genitalia, which indicates our sex) has developed as female, then that child will identify as female regardless of the other variables. Added to this is the fact that gender identity is fixed at between 3-4 (Gooren et al) years of age and cannot be altered thereafter. And it is precisely these facts that the objectors ignore.

It is probable there are those within the health service who have previously declined to become involved in providing treatment for patients diagnosed with GID, and this may be due to their own lack of understanding as to the true clinical nature of the condition and the basis for the prescribed treatment path. There is some solace (though not much) in the fact that this is not the only condition that has been disputed by the medical professions. There was a time when members of the medical, psychological and psychiatric professions were sceptical about conditions like Irritable Bowel Syndrome, M.E. (Myalgic Encephalomyelitis), or Chronic Fatigue Syndrome (the yuppie flu!), to name a few; as all too many sufferers can confirm from their own experience. In fairness to medical professionals within the health service, there is sufficient evidence to show that there simply wasn't the necessary awareness of this condition, to enable them to engage with this patient group. Some may justly point out though that the information has been available for a considerable period of time and that those who were engaging with this patient group might have been more forthright in raising awareness amongst their colleagues. Whatever the case may be, there are signs that this situation has improved significantly in recent times. This is also reflected in the way the media cover stories relating to people with GID.

The reality remains that there is still a significant gap in terms of awareness and training; between what is currently available to those working within the health services and what they really need in order to provide anything like adequate healthcare to this patient group. This deficiency exists across the public sector as a whole and much needs to be done to correct the situation. This has led to (what the author believes to be) a great deal of *unintentional* discrimination against people with GID, and consequently, their families. This has undoubtedly exacerbated the difficulties of this patient group and has only helped to reinforce the stigma suffered by them on a daily basis.

If this condition is ever to be recognised within mainstream medicine, and for that matter within mainstream society, and if people with GID are to receive the appropriate healthcare, then those with the resources and the authority, must be properly informed about the condition and from there put in place the appropriate treatments and legal changes required to help this patient group. This is essential in order to safeguard their rights citizens, as well as those of their families. The reason for mentioning this here is that despite there being widespread recognition of GID across the world and in particular the member states within the Council of Europe, people with GID in this country are still being denied access to appropriate healthcare. This raises a serious human rights issue with regards to this patient group.

In this chapter we looked at the nature and causes of a number of intersex conditions and of Gender Identity Disorder in particular. It was shown that the *clinical* evidence for GID as an intersex condition is now well established. Not only this, but it is a clinically diagnosable congenital condition over which the individual has absolutely no control. It is not, as some believe, a choice made by the individual to change into a member of the opposite sex, nor is it a matter of arriving home from work one day and telling their spouse, that they fancy becoming a woman or a man, nor for that matter that they feel like having a sex change; as it is so often portrayed by some sections of the media. On the contrary, it is a condition that many would rather suffer in silence; living in a constant state of distress and social dysfunction and in a high percentage of cases, attempt suicide, rather than face the humiliation and rejection of their families, friends, work colleagues etc.

It was mentioned earlier in the Preface that there has been an announcement reported in the Times in December of 2009, of an international team of scientists who identified ,the gene that keeps females female.? They have discovered that when they artificially switched off the gene in adult female mice their ovaries began to develop into male testes and their testosterone levels were similar to those of healthy male mice. The gene in question is known as FOXL2.

It was also noted that one aspect of this discovery is particularly interesting insofar as the gene being located on ,non-sex chromosome? (my emphasis). It is believed that this is going to dramatically affect the way in which gender reassignment treatments are carried our in the future, but this has yet to be researched further. This new evidence regarding the effects of genes and chromosomes on gender and gender identity not only reinforces the fact that Gender Identity Disorder is not a sex or sexual condition, but that its association with anything relating to sex and sexuality is wholly inappropriate and even dangerous.

In looking forward to the chapter on the legal issues affecting people with GID, legislators are duty bound to consider this evidence along with all the other evidence relating to GID when drafting the appropriate legislation, as per their commitment in the new Programme for Government.

In the next chapter we will look at how GID is diagnosed and the treatment options available to people once they've been diagnosed. We will then go on to look at what life is like for those who decide to proceed with full gender reassignment.

Chapter Three

DIAGNOSIS AND TREATMENT OF
GENDER IDENTITY DISORDER

Naturam expelles furca, tamen usque recurret. You may drive out nature with a pitchfork, yet she will be constantly running back.

Horace

Problems with Diagnosing Gender Identity Disorder

Gender Identity Disorder has become easier to diagnose in recent years, despite the slowness of some within the medical profession to recognise it. Even the general public show a growing awareness of this condition and are increasingly more understanding towards those who struggle with it.

One of the reasons the diagnosis is becoming easier is the increasing numbers of people who are presenting with a variety of distinctive psychological and behavioural characteristics which are more consistent with the gender they identify with as opposed to the one assigned at birth. These characteristics are also clearly distinguishable from transvestites and crossdressers etc. In fact these distinctions are extremely important, not just for the purpose of diagnosis, but also for treatment. It is an essential requirement in diagnosis to ascertain whether there are any mental or psychological problems, which may be termed *contra-indicators*. Where such *contra-indicators* are identified then a different diagnosis is normally the outcome. This includes the possibility that the person presenting for diagnosis has another type of disorder which is not related to a Gender Identity Disorder or other related intersex conditions.

Part of the problem with diagnosing Gender Identity Disorder, has been the ongoing **nature-nurture** debate that still rages within psychology and psychiatry and the effects this has on diagnostic methodologies and subsequent treatments. Some within these professions have attributed GID to nothing more than environmental influences, e.g. parental influences, especially of the mother over the child. According to these theories boys can be feminised through over-exposure to their mothers and other females during the earlier years and that this leads to confusion in later life and the difficulties they experience regarding their gender identity. On the face of it this seems like a plausible position, however the problem with it is that it doesn't fit for those who never experienced over-exposure to their mother and other females. In fact people with GID can testify that they were brought up as every other boy in the family and were taught to behave in every respect like other boys; the difference being they never really identified themselves in the same way. In other words, people with GID will state that they were expected to conform in exact accordance with their assigned gender role, despite their own sense of disconnection from it.

Diagnosing GID

People with GID, whether male or female, are diagnosed after several or more assessments by a qualified clinical psychologist or consultant psychiatrist, It is only after other possible disorders have been eliminated that Gender Identity Disorder is diagnosed. The diagnosis is based on the persons concerned demonstrating persistent and distinctive gender characteristics and behaviours, which cannot be attributed to any of the other disorders. This must persist for a period of two or more years. These characteristics can include:

• A very strong and persistent feeling of living in the wrong gender. This must be present for a minimum of two years prior to diagnosis.

• A strong and persistent desire to live and be accepted in the opposite gender to that assigned at birth.

• People with GID also have very distinct conflicts with their genitalia, i.e. there is an overriding sense of discomfort and distress from having the wrong genitalia. For many this is one of the most dramatic indicators and is a cause of deep distress and depression. This problem can be so profound that some people have been known to castrate themselves or at least contemplate doing so in order to have the same genital features of the identified gender.

• Preferring to dress and live as a female rather than a male and vice-versa. In other words, dressing in a manner consistent with the gender to which the person identifies as their true gender.

• A distinct preference for living in the opposite social gender role, i.e. having a distinct preference for socialising in female company rather than male, and vice-versa.

These indicators go well beyond the typical fetish type indicators manifest amongst transvestites and crossdresser's, and the entertainment value for drag queens. Whereas transvestites and crossdresser's derive some gratification or release from stress, and dress on the basis of compulsion, which can be psycho sexual in nature, people with GID seek only to wear what is for them the more appropriate clothing for their gender. The difference is *fundamental* to our pre-conceived ideas of *men* who dress as women!

It is worth repeating here that it can take a considerable amount of time before a diagnosis is given, and it *must* be based upon the elimination of other possible explanations or disorders. It is extremely important to note, that when a diagnosis is made it must then be confirmed by another qualified psychiatrist or psychologist. As stated earlier this will normally be a clinical psychologist or consultant psychiatrist. Once the diagnosis has been confirmed the various treatment options are considered.

Treatment of Gender Identity Disorder

Once a diagnosis has been made and confirmed referral is then made to an Endocrinologist for the purpose of commencing hormone treatment. However, before treatment can commence a full medical check-up must be carried out to ensure that there are no health concerns. Non-surgical treatment options for Male-to-Females can include some or all of the following:

- Hormone Treatment
- Counselling
- Psychotherapy

- Electrolysis/Laser Treatment
- Speech Therapy
- Deportment

Some people diagnosed with GID are content to settle for counselling or therapy and continue living in their assigned gender at birth. Some may also live between the two genders, periodically dressing according to their preferred gender. The reasons for this can be quite complex and compelling and are often based upon family, work, legal and social considerations.

On the other hand many People with GID opt for complete gender reassignment, including **Genital Realignment Surgery** (GRS). This can include the above treatments plus hormone treatment and the following surgeries:

For Male to Female Patients:

- Penectomy (removal of the penis)
- Orchidectomy (removal of testes)
- Vaginoplasty (Construction of a vagina)
- Clitoroplasty (construction of the clitoris)
- Breast Augmentation (increased breast size)
- Rhinoplasty (reshaping the nose)
- Cosmetic Surgeries, e.g. facial remodelling, hair transplants
- Thyroid Chondroplasty (shaving of the Adam's Apple)
- Crico-Thyroid Approximation and Anterior Commisure Advancement.

For Female-to-Male Patients:

- Hysterectomy and Oophorectomy (removal of uterus and ovaries)
- Bilateral Mastectomy (breast removal)
- Phalloplasty (construction of a penis)

Prior to surgery taking place, the patient is referred to an endocrinologist to commence hormone treatment. Before hormone treatment can commence however, numerous blood tests have to be completed in order to ensure that the patient is in sufficient health to enable them to proceed with the treatment. These tests include existing hormone levels, liver function, lymphocytes, calcium etc. The list is quite extensive and necessary. Treatment starts by gradually building up oestrogens in the body, for male-to-female and testosterone for female-to-male. Once the patient is adapting well to the new hormones the dosage is increased to a level consistent to that of normal levels in biological females and males.

After some time and during a successful transition period the male-to-female patient is then put onto anti-androgens such as Androcur and Zoladex. Zoladex is administered by injection through the stomach. Anti-androgens reduce the male hormones and are used prior to Genital Realignment Surgery (GRS). This hormone treatment can adversely affect the patient's libido, which for some can be a high price to pay. Patients, who choose to proceed, do so knowing the probable effects on their libido. This is completely contrary to one of the most common and hurtful allegations about why people with GID go through gender reassignment, i.e. to fulfil some sexual fantasy.

While on hormone treatment the person can go through many emotional swings while their body adapts to the new hormones. There is also the potential for other side effects such as blood clots forming, which may require taking Aspirin on a daily basis.

One of the most significant challenges for the GID person is the Real Life Experience (RLE), also known as the Real Life Test; the latter term is greatly disliked by many GID people. They prefer the former term or another known as *Transition*. Entering the Real Life Experience means to live in the role of the opposite social gender for a period of two years. This is to see if the patient can successfully transition and live in their new social gender role. This can be far more traumatic than any hormone treatment or surgical procedure and can be make-or-break when it comes to living permanently in the new gender role. It takes the most extraordinary courage for a GID person to enter family, work and public life living in the opposite social gender role to the one people are already familiar. However there are some who are so well adapted to their new gender role that they do not want to wait the required full two years before surgery.

There are so many things that can and do go wrong and the price for taking such a courageous step can be extraordinarily high. This is one of the reasons why *transioning* over a period of two years is so important. It gives time to adjust to the new social gender role and be better prepared for the final and most dramatic stage of all: Genital Realignment Surgery (GRS); so called because it replaces the existing genitalia with those of their new gender. This procedure is easier to perform on male-to-females than it is for female-to-males. However it is much easier for female-to-males to transition visually than for male-to-females.

When female-to-males undergo male hormone treatment they experience very dramatic changes that make it far easier for them to integrate into society, at worst they can expect to look like effeminate males or gender neutral. Their voices deepen and they grow facial hair and in some cases have receding hairlines, similar to biological males, thus enabling them to integrate more easily. The majority of male–to-females on the other hand have a more difficult transition and stand out far more, especially on account of their strong male facial structure, Adam's apple, facial hair, etc. Also, it is harder to hide their voices, male mannerisms and posture. This all serves to make life very stressful indeed. This is in addition to having to face their families, friends, employers, work colleagues and the wider public. It also explains why male-to-Females are so often mistaken for transvestites and are exposed to so much intolerance, ridicule and rejection. This makes it an essential requirement for people with GID to have strong support systems in place, especially in the way of therapy, counselling, family, peer and group support, adequate information, financial resources etc. if they are to have a successful transition.

One of the most shocking and deeply distressing aspects of this condition is the extremes to which some people with GID will go in order to fulfil their need to live within their true gender identity. As mentioned earlier, it is known that some people have been reduced to such low despair they will literally castrate themselves in order to have what is for them the right body. Female-to-males have been known to carry out their own mastectomies, while male-to-females have performed self-castration, i.e. remove their male genitals. Others pay for their own surgeries and go abroad to private clinics that will perform operations without the need to complete their real life experience. But these are fraught with potential problems, especially were there are post-operative complications, some of which can be life threatening. It would be so easy to criticise such people as being reckless and irresponsible. However, it should be borne in mind that there is very little support or care within the Health Service at present and the people concerned are in the most awful states of desperation and despair because they believe they will never receive the treatment they need. Even when they do, the cost of surgery within the EU is so prohibitive for most that they feel they have no choice but to go further afield in order to have their genital reassignment surgery carried out. The numbers going abroad for surgery is quite significant and should be a cause for serious concern. The more extreme cases are thankfully rare, but they are significant and they do serve to highlight the great need there is for the Health Service Executive to grasp the seriousness of the situation and start putting the necessary healthcare facilities in place.

It has been known for some who have gone through GRS to have regrets afterwards and have sought a reversal of their surgery. However, it should be borne in mind that up to 97% of those who have had full GRS have gone on to live fulfilling lives within their new gender roles and enjoy the normality of life that GRS can bring. However a note of caution is required here, in that it is *strongly* recommended that those seeking GRS, or breast augmentation, including hormone therapy, should complete the transition into their new social gender role. This is absolutely essential if these individuals are to avoid having regrets post-surgery. Those who do have surgery without completing the transition stage leave themselves open to the possibility of regretting it later on. They also do a great disservice to those who seek to complete their transition and go on to have their surgery, in that they raise doubts in the minds of medical professionals and the wider public about the wisdom of permitting this extreme type of surgery.

Another difficulty in coming to terms with a diagnosis of GID (from the patient's perspective) is the unclear manner in which the diagnosis is presented. This makes it very difficult for them to understand their own condition and in turn affects how well informed, or, uninformed they may be when considering the most appropriate treatment. This difficulty is exacerbated for those who must live within a society, which has very little awareness of this condition. This has an extremely important bearing upon how they cope with the condition and if and how they disclose it to their families, friends, employers etc. It is absolutely essential therefore that people with GID be given as much factual information as possible, and in as simple a language as possible. Lives really are at risk at both the pre and post diagnosis stages. Marriages and family relationships along with employment, acceptance within peer groups, the workplace etc. are also factors to be taken into account before any decisions can be made on whether to proceed with any of the treatment options. <u>Each one must be able to decide on a treatment option that accommodates his or her own specific life situation.</u>

It really is worth repeating that GID is a congenital disorder and that people are born with this condition just as other people are born with other congenital conditions such as Asthma, Spina Bifida, Cerebral Palsy etc.; conditions for which the sufferers would never be expected to justify, themselves or, apologise to anyone; in fact we would think this to be an utterly preposterous suggestion. And so too it should be with any congenital condition, including an intersex condition like GID.

One of the most difficult decisions to be made is whether or not to disclose the condition to a spouse. This is especially problematic where a spouse may already have indicated prejudice and intolerance towards others with the condition. There is so much to lose on the part of the person making the disclosure that they could be easily forgiven for putting it off. The majority of people with GID would prefer to keep their families intact both before and after they make their disclosure. The reality for these people is that they are most likely to lose their families and a great deal more besides.This flies in the face of much of the harmful and deeply hurtful accusations that are spread about people with GID regarding their motives for proceeding with genital realignment surgery. At all times the emphasis must be on the issue of gender identity and *not* anything that is of a sexual nature or sexual orientation.

Treatment of GID and transitioning are very personal to each individual and can vary widely in terms of their progress and outcome; from the very positive to the deeply distressing, to the point where it becomes life-threatening. We will look at these themes in greater detail in the next chapter. The most important thing to realise here is that no one would go through all this if it wasn't really necessary. And for some, it is undoubtedly the most frightening and at the same time, the most courageous things they will ever do in their lives.

Accessing Healthcare in Ireland

People with GID find it extraordinarily difficult or impossible to access adequate healthcare for their condition and so for the most part are condemned to live in bodies that conflict with their true gender identity. Many People with GID can testify to being dismissed out of hand by their G.P. Things are so bad that it is regarded as a major achievement to find a sympathetic G.P. who can then refer a patient on to a qualified clinical psychologist or consultant psychiatrist, and harder still to receive treatment from an endocrinologist. And even when they do eventually begin to receive treatment, the lengths they have to go to in order to get full Gender Realignment Surgery simply beggars belief. It is because of this that many people have been left in limbo and have to find the resources from somewhere in order to go abroad and have their Gender Realignment Surgery. Many have had to resort to saving or getting themselves into serious debt. Then they must face the added problem of travelling abroad, more often as far away as Thailand, in order to have their surgery. As mentioned earlier, this is mainly due to the cost of surgery within Europe being so prohibitive. There are very serious risks in having this surgery performed so far from home, especially if complications should arise, as they have done with some. There have been some who have had life threatening complications and have found it difficult to get the right treatment at home in Ireland. This is due primarily to the almost complete lack of knowledge towards towards this type of surgery within the Irish health service.

The following two cases will demonstrate what can happen when people become so desperate they feel they have no choice but to take matters into their own hands. The names used are fictitious but the cases are factual.

Case A (Mary)

Mary is a male-to-female person with GID. She had received a medical diagnosis from a qualified psychiatrist and began her hormone treatment almost immediately. However Mary's consultant died prematurely and Mary was left with no one to provide her with the ongoing treatment she needed to complete her gender reassignment. Mary had not started her Real Life Experience and had also failed to inform her family, friends etc. of her diagnosis. She decided to take redundancy from her job and use the redundancy to travel to Thailand and have her genital realignment surgery there. As mentioned earlier, Mary never informed any of her family or friends about either her diagnosis or her intention to go abroad to have the surgery. The first they knew about it was on Mary's arrival home. Mary had informed them that she was travelling to Thailand on holiday. So it was a complete shock for her family and friends when they were greeted by a woman rather than the man who had left the country. The family were understandably shocked and deeply upset by the situation and were at a complete loss as to how to react. Their shock quickly turned to anger and they refused to accept Mary in her new female gender.

Mary was left in a state of despair and isolation and without any support from her family and friends; the very thing she needed most if she was to integrate into the community in which she lived. Understandably though, the news of what had happened quickly spread and as it did Mary found herself in greater isolation. However, the worst was yet to come. Mary became increasingly depressed and isolated and began to experience suicidal thoughts. Mary developed a very serious infection in her new vagina and required immediate hospitalisation.

The medical team attending her had never dealt with this kind of situation before and so were at a loss as to how to treat Mary. Her situation deteriorated rapidly and she went into a coma in which she remained for several weeks. During this time some of her family and friends rallied round and when Mary eventually came out of her coma was taken into psychiatric care where she stayed until she was able to return home. Eventually Mary started to live some kind of a life in her new gender role, but it is fair to say that she still has a long road ahead before she will be able to live a fully functional and happy life.

Case B (Lisa)

This case was reported in the Irish Journal of Medical Science, September 2001, from the Department of Urology, St James's Hospital, Dublin, and involves the patient self-castrating.

Lisa was diagnosed with GID and opted to go the conventional treatment route. The problem for Lisa was that she was not receiving the treatment she needed so she was left in a medical limbo. The wait for genital realignment surgery became intolerable, and as so often happens in these cases Lisa became severely depressed. Over time Lisa's situation became so desperate that she took the most drastic step that could be taken, next to suicide; she castrated herself. One can hardly imagine the state of mind she must have been in and the utter desperation she felt that would drive her to such drastic measures in order that she could live her life in a way and with the body that was most normal for her.

Both of these cases beg the question: what civilised society can think it acceptable that people diagnosed with any medical condition should be so neglected by their health service that they feel they have no option but to resort to such drastic measures, including risking their own lives? As the journal states:

Deliberate genital self-mutilation is rare. Successful self-castration has been reported in a small number of individuals… This study reports one such case of self-castration in a transsexual who was dissatisfied with waiting times for sex reassignment surgery (SRS)… The apparent triggering factor in this case appears to be depression related to the lengthy waiting times for SRS. *As neither psychotherapy nor hormonal manipulation is successful, consideration should be given to improving the resources for patients with genuine gender dysmorphism (my emphasis).*[18]

What both of these cases have in common is the serious lack of adequate healthcare for people with Gender Identity Disorder and the desperate plight in which they too often find themselves. In quite a significant number of the cases known to the author, the patients feel they have no option but to take out large loans in order to fund their own treatments, which they can ill afford to do. But they will do this rather than allow themselves to be cast into the medical limbo in which so many still are to this day. Another major problem is the lack of qualified practitioners who can diagnose the condition and provide appropriate hormone treatment. Two of the most dangerous consequences of this are self-diagnosis and self-medication. In cases where those who self-diagnose and self-medicate, they will purchase hormones through the internet and administer them without any qualified medical supervision.

As one can imagine, people in this situation are extremely vulnerable and are prey to all manner of negative influences.

New Treatment Pathway

There is good news on the horizon though, in that there is a recommended Treatment Pathway that will see GID patients through from initial referral from their G.P. to post-surgical care. The Treatment Pathway includes the following stages:

1. Referral from G.P. to Clinical Psychologist / Psychiatrist
2. Assessment by Clinical Psychologist / Psychiatrist
3. Referral for Second Opinion from Clinical Psychologist/Psychiatrist
4. Referral to Endocrinologist to commence Hormonal Treatment and monitoring
5. Referral for Surgical Intervention and GRS
6. Post GRS Care and Support
7. Long-Term Care (where appropriate).

It is also recommended that there is an adequate counselling service available for the GID patient throughout the treatment process. This counselling service should also be made available to their families in order to help them to make the necessary adjustments to the new situation.

Legal Action

A number of people have had to take legal action against the former Health Boards in order to get the funding for their surgeries. This unnecessary action can cost far more in legal costs than the actual payment towards the realignment surgery. Part of the problem has been in how the Health Service and medical practitioners view genital realignment surgery, breast augmentation, laser treatment etc., and whether they view this as nothing more than elective forms of surgery; despite the fact that such patients have been diagnosed with a congenital condition and are *prescribed* this form of treatment and other medical and surgical interventions. Of course one of the principle reasons is cost. However the good news is that things are changing and it is possible for patients with GID to receive funding for their treatments. This is for those treatments that are not available in Ireland and where the patient has to travel abroad. Surgeries funded by the HSE is normally carried out at Charing Cross Hospital in the UK.

The Role of Language

Medical professionals in this country who provide diagnoses for patients with GID seem oblivious to the serious negative impact that terms such as *Transgenderism* and *Transsexualism* can have and they often fail to take this into consideration when advising patients who are in the process of making their disclosure. This can have a major effect upon how people respond to such disclosures and it can make a significant difference to how people subsequently perceive both the condition and those who disclose it.

Consultants, GP's and counsellors etc., have a very

significant role to play in how patients make their disclosure of GID. Having a professional input will not only help those making the disclosure but it will also help the spouses, partners, and children etc. to gain a better understanding of the condition. Unfortunately this option is not widely available. It is extremely important that it is made available, as the benefits can be quite considerable for all concerned. For example, professional intervention can help keep the disclosure on a medical level, which is critically important for future outcomes.

Reverting to Original Gender

Some of those patients who have undergone genital realignment surgery do change their minds afterwards and express regret at having had the surgery. The author is not aware of any specific case in Ireland but is aware that it has occurred in an extremely small percentage of cases.

Those who oppose the idea of any form of gender reassignment and especially genital realignment surgery, quickly seize upon these very rare incidents and use them as evidence to uphold their own views. And they use these rare cases as a basis for dissuading those who are planning to go through GRS from doing so. They conveniently disregard the vast majority who are more than happy with the outcome of their surgery and the fact that it has allowed them for the first time to go on and live normal lives.

Objectors also ignore the fact that some of those who seek to reverse their GRS may not actually deny or regret their diagnosis. It may in fact be more a case regretting the negative consequences that follow from making a disclosure and while they go through their real life experience in the their new social gender role. In other words, it may be more to do with the refusal of others to accept them in their new gender. What people too often forget is that those who go through with GRS pay a very high price for doing so, which involves great personal loss. Some of those expressing regret feel compelled to do so due to deep psychological, social and economic pressures that they have to endure, and in most cases without any adequate support systems or structures in place. This can happen before or after GRS. This failure will inevitably cause extreme difficulties for those individuals, which others could not even begin to imagine. Once again this highlights the need for a greater awareness and understanding of GID as a whole and the need to respect and support those who make the decision to go through gender reassignment, which let us remember is *the* prescribed treatment process for this condition.

Chapter Four

LIFE WITH GENDER IDENTITY DISORDER

A Life Not lived

GID in Childhood

Living with GID means to live in a continual state of conflict and distress, borne out of a strong sense of being a female in a male body, or vice-versa. It means trying to live as a boy when you know (or at least have a sense) that you *are* a girl; trying to play with the boys when all you really want to do is play with other girls. It means not merely disliking the clothes you wear, because they're not pretty and girlie enough, but knowing they're just not appropriate. It means wanting to play with your sisters and the girls next door rather than play with your brothers and *boy* friends. It means identifying more with your sisters and other girls emotionally than you do with your brothers and other boys. It means knowing you are different, but without the knowledge of why you are different. And worse still is the fact that no one else knows either.

Children learn from an early age the role of conditional love and that conformity is one of those conditions. Can they articulate it? Not always, but they definitely sense it and so they conform, because they want to be loved, and being loved means obeying mammy and daddy and fitting in with their brothers and sisters and friends. It means fitting in at school in the hope that they will be accepted and no one will be nasty to them. And it is precisely this need to be loved and to fit in that makes them conform, to the point where they suppress their true gender identity and force (repress) themselves into living in the gender assigned to them at birth. How can that be dishonest? Yet that is precisely what children with GID will be accused of as they get older. It is completely unfair and it places an intolerable burden upon these children, which affects them throughout the remainder of their lives.

While some children may succeed in suppressing their true gender identity, others cannot, not for the want of trying, but because the identity is already so strong and undeniable that it is simply impossible to hide it. Some of the opposite gender behaviours manifest themselves unbeknown to the child. For example, being unusually sensitive for a boy, being very chatty and crying easily, despite the strong male influence to be hard etc; *boy's don't cry* and all that nonsense. Then there is the natural desire to wear the clothes of the opposite gender etc. Girls do have a greater natural sensitivity than boys and it should be recognised as such. The problem is that boys with GID receive a lot of bullying in the form of name calling, being ostracised and beatings etc. The same is true for some girls with GID. Can it really be any surprise then that those children who have a sense of being different - but without knowing why they are different and experience so much mis-understanding and harsh treatment, that those same children should not try to protect themselves at all costs; even if that means suppressing their most natural instinct to live within their true gender identity.

From childhood on children are faced with so many pressures and threats to conform to their families, societies, religions and the States expectations about who they are and what they ought to be. This has changed in so many ways in recent times, but not when it comes to our gender and sex. The assumption remains that person's gender is as black and white an issue as it has always been, despite all the evidence to the contrary.

Children are also thought from the earliest age that terrible things will happen to them if they don't tell the truth. But when you struggle with a condition like GID and you try to tell people about it, you learn very quickly that terrible things *do* happen when you *tell the truth!* This is what the Americans describe as a *double whammy*. In other words, you are damned if you tell the truth and you're damned if you don't. Because of this it should be easy to recognise the incredible courage necessary to tell people that you are different. This is an incredibly difficult thing for adults to do, let alone a child. Especially when they already sense that they will be blamed, ridiculed, condemned and suffer rejection from family and friends etc. It should be no surprise then that many children with GID, even if they could articulate it, would rather try to conform than get into trouble by insisting that they be raised as girls rather than boys and vice-versa. This seems so much easier and safer than facing the hurt of telling mammy and daddy they are not a boy but a girl, knowing that it is completely unacceptable to their parents.

However, it is far too simplistic to suggest that parents should automatically recognise their child's behaviour and character traits as indicating GID, and thereby accept the child's assertions to be living in the wrong body. But it is equally wrong to suggest that parents should ignore what their children are telling them and what is evident in their behaviour. Nor should they try to force their children to continue living within their assigned birth gender. What should be done is to have the child properly assessed in order to find out what exactly is going on and what makes them so convinced that they are living in the wrong body. To do this parents must put their own feelings and prejudices to one side and do what is best for the child; for it is ultimately the *child* who must go on and live as normal and happy a life as possible within their own gender and not the one assigned to them by others. This brings us to an extremely important question: can children of four and five years of age really *know* that they are of the opposite gender to the one in which they are being raised? The answer is emphatically, yes they can!

To demonstrate this I refer the reader to an ABC production of 20/20, which was presented by the renowned American journalist Barbara Walters, in which she interviewed three children with GID and their parents. To say that these children and their parents are remarkable would be an understatement. They are all heroes and their stories are worthy of our attention.

For the purposes of this section we will look at one of the children highlighted. Her name is Jazz and she's a GID male to female. As young as two years of age Jazz was showing the clearest signs of discomfort at being raised as a boy. From the earliest age Jazz was showing her discomfort with wearing boy's clothes. In one instance when Jazz was just 15 months old *"he would unsnap his onesies (babygrow) to make it look like a dress.* When the parents referred to her as a *good boy,* Jazz would correct them by saying that she was a girl. As time went on Jazz was more inclined towards *girl's things,* such as painting her nails, playing with girls toys and even asserting that she should not have a penis.

Her parents wanted to believe that this was just a phase

and that it would pass, but it didn't and they were then left with a dilemma as to what they should do next. As they became more troubled by their child's behaviour, they came across the Diagnostic and Statistical Manual (DSM-IV), which to their amazement exactly described all of the symptoms or indicators of Gender Identity Disorder. This was a major turning point for them and for the first time they managed to get a hold on the situation. Jazz's parents then spoke with their paediatrician who told them that Jazz did indeed have Gender Identity Disorder and referred them on to a specialist in GID.

After the parent's received the diagnosis of GID they then explained the situation to their other children. They also allowed Jazz to dress more frequently in girls clothes, but still referred to her as *he*, which was quite upsetting for her. Eventually the parents allowed Jazz to wear a swimsuit and explained to the other children who came to the house to play, that though Jazz was a boy, she wanted to be a girl. They fully accepted the explanation given and simply got on with being Jazz's friends. Children can be remarkably accepting in ways that adults are not.

Space does not allow for the complete story to be told here, but I would strongly recommend that readers get to see this powerful and deeply moving programme. What can be said in conclusion to this story is, the amazing unconditional love and acceptance demonstrated by Jazz's parents and the example and inspiration they are to the parents of children with GID everywhere. Because of the way in which they responded to Jazz and despite the long hard road ahead, this little girl has every possibility of living as normal and happy a life as possible. What was also deeply moving in this story was the way in which the parents could also deal with the pain of their own loss. They were not losing a child, but they were losing a son and that is a genuine cause for grief, as is any great loss. What makes these parent's exceptional though is, the manner in which they dealt with their own grief and pain separately and out of sight from Jazz's need to be accepted and loved for who she is. It is because of this unconditional love that this most beautiful little girl can now look forward to a much brighter and happier future.

When we really think about it, why would any child of two years of age or even older, *choose* to live in the opposite gender? And why should it occur to any child to justify what comes most naturally to them? The answer is, that it doesn't occur to them; and why should it. They're children; children with GID. Children with GID are just like every other child in this respect; and like every other child, they become aware of how unacceptable their behaviour is from external sources, i.e. parents, siblings, friends, teachers etc. And this is precisely the point at which the gender conflicts that will last a lifetime begin. This is also why it is so important for children who display the traits so consistent with GID, that they should receive the earliest possible intervention. This will enable them to develop a positive gender identity over time and to avoid the type of dysfunctional living that will otherwise follow later on.

GID and Adolescence

An exceptionally difficult stage of our development is adolescence (which adult society too quickly forgets) and the development of self identity and individuality; sexual awareness; peer group pressure; coping with society's expectations; demands for greater conformity and stereotyping us within our assigned gender roles. These and many other pressures are unfairly put upon the shoulders of young teenagers. Adults are barely able to cope with these pressures yet we think nothing of putting them on young people who are simply not able to deal with them. Teenagers become more acutely aware of the problems they face if they don't conform. For example, when young adolescent boys behave in ways that are considered feminine, they are automatically assumed to be gay or very effeminate and in the case of girls behaving inappropriately, they are considered to be *tomboys* or lesbians. In many cases boys and girls outgrow these behaviours, but in others they don't, or if they do outgrow them, then it is due to the negative reinforcements they receive from their parents, siblings, teachers and especially their peers. These are often seen as insurmountable forces to overcome, especially where there is violence, verbal and emotional abuse involved. Teenage boys who display sensitive characteristics are often picked on in school and singled out as being odd or freakish. Other sensitive teenagers may see this and work doubly hard at hiding their sensitive nature and do their best to fit in and be accepted. This makes it almost impossible for teenagers to disclose their problems to anyone, especially *not* to those, within what should be, their most important support structures. The consequences of this are that these teenagers find themselves completely cut off and isolated.

The onset of puberty is a total nightmare for Gender Dysphoric adolescents. On top of the normal problems that teenagers experience e.g. the start of menstruation for girls and the growth of hair in places that make them feel freaky and scared, there are problems with acne and irrational mood swings. It is all of this and more for the gender dysphoric teenager. For example, if you are a GID girl, imagine waking up one morning to discover that you are starting to grow facial hair when your internalised expectation is that you shouldn't. When you know you're supposed to have a period, but don't! When you expect to have breasts like other girls, but they don't grow. And most traumatic of all, imagine developing more pronounced male genitalia where you think there should be none. It is exactly the same for female to males; having to cope with missing sex organs. GID males expect to develop a penis rather than a vagina and they don't expect or want to develop breasts. It is almost impossible to avoid feeling abnormal, freakish and unacceptable. It really is very difficult to describe just how abnormal it feels to have your body *not* develop the way you expect it to. This is just a part of what it is like for teenagers who struggle to live with GID.

It is extremely difficult for teenagers with GID to fit in with their schoolmates and they suffer in many ways when their peers discover that they believe themselves to be in the wrong body. Such disclosures leave the teenager with GID extremely vulnerable to bullying, harassment and violence. This contributes to the numbers of teenagers who consider or succeed in taking their own lives every year in this country.

It seems to be the universal expectation that adolescent teenagers are normally sullen and withdrawn; that they will inevitably be grumpy and uncooperative and that being rebellious is a *given* that has to be endured rather than understood. This is especially true of those teenagers who are struggling with their gender identity and for that matter teenager's who struggle with their sexuality. The fact is that any child or teenager, who feels unsafe and unable to confide in their parents, siblings, friends teachers etc. are far more likely to go into themselves in order to try and protect themselves from being hurt and rejected.

No child, regardless of their age should have to endure this kind of pressure and torment. But this regrettably is what results from the unrealistic expectations that society has towards its teenage population. Why for example are teenagers expected to behave like adults when coping with life's problems, while adults find those same problems difficult to cope with? This is not only intolerable for teenagers, it is unreasonable and downright irresponsible; one might even say that it is a form of emotional and mental cruelty. Why wouldn't they withdraw into themselves when they quite literally feel that they are unable to cope and have nowhere else to turn for help?

While it is true that GID is not a disability per se, it is extremely debilitating. We know for example that teenagers with GID will most likely never fulfil their true potential so long as they try to conform to the opposite gender. Another example of how debilitating GID can be is in relationships. They are fraught with difficulties and tensions for those who have to live with the condition. Dating and indeed who to date is a cause of great confusion and distress. Who should they hang out with in college; should they continue to conform or should they try to live within their true gender identity? Who do they speak to about the fact that they don't have the right body parts and functions? Who can they trust with this, and who won't make them feel like complete nut cases or freaks? To compound this even further, they have to live with this condition in total silence and secrecy for most of their lives. Not receiving the recognition and interventions needed at this stage has deeply profound consequences for them and their future. It is estimated that children with GID who are rejected by their families are four times more likely to commit suicide than the rest of the teenage population. They are also more likely to turn to drugs as a way of coping and as a consequence live very dysfunctional lives; opting to live in the shadows and fringes of society because they do not fit in anywhere else, because they're not allowed to fit in.[19]

For other teenagers with GID the only source of help is the LGBT community. They are attracted to these communities because they are the only places in which to feel safe; to feel accepted. But this is really not appropriate for these teenagers as their issue is not one of sexual orientation but of gender identity and it can create even further confusion for them. That said; those who provide safe places for these teenagers are to be highly commended for creating safe environments that otherwise would not exist. It is no exaggeration to say that these *safe places* are most probably saving the lives of these teenagers. Ultimately though the responsibility for these children, (for they are still children,) must lie with their parents. It is the duty of parents to provide safe homes for their children. It is also the responsibility of parents to do everything in their power to protect their children and if this means going outside of the home to get that help then that is what they must do. Where a child discloses that he or she is living in the wrong body, those parents have a duty of care to their children, to make sure they are properly informed about Gender Identity Disorder and to provide whatever support is necessary to protect their children from harm. We will look at this in greater detail later. For now let it be acknowledged that there is nothing any child with GID wants more than to be unconditionally loved and accepted by their own families and this starts with mum and dad.

GID in Adulthood

We come now to adults with Gender Identity Disorder and to the questions they are most frequently asked when they disclose their diagnosis or their belief that they have a problem with their gender identity. The two questions they are most likely to be asked are: *why did it take you so long to tell someone?* And *why then did you get married and have children?* On the face of it these do seem like perfectly reasonable questions, however this is not always true. It is too often the case that those who ask these questions have an ulterior motive and more often than not such questions are put in the form of an accusation against the person making a disclosure. The accusation is normally that the person making the disclosure has been acting dishonestly and was deliberately deceiving everyone around them. These and other questions are not always motivated by an effort to understand the condition, and the reasons why there hasn't been an earlier disclosure. But rather it is about finding a reason to justify the blame, ridicule and rejection that invariably follows a disclosure of this kind. In other words, there is no attempt whatsoever to understand that the adult making the disclosure is merely continuing on from their childhood and adolescence and may not be any more aware of why exactly they feel that they are living in the wrong body. People conveniently forget that these adults are every bit as vulnerable and fearful as they were when they were teenagers; and children before that. They fail to realise that this is a condition that has stayed with them throughout their entire lives. As we will see later this kind of reaction can have the most awful consequences for all concerned.

Such is the force of society's expectations and family

demands for conformity that adults with GID will try their level best to conform and fulfil the expectations placed upon them. So they try to fit into *normal* lives, *normal* relationships, *normal* family life, *normal* work life and *normal* functioning within their communities. They very genuinely believe, and want to believe, that they can overcome this problem if they put it to the back of their minds and get on with living a *normal* life. But sooner or later this all becomes untenable and something inevitably gives; that something is different to each individual. For example, while many try to live within the marital relationship and raise children, there may be some traumatic event that leads the person to the conclusion that they can no longer live a *false* life and must therefore do something to rectify the situation. For others it can be a gradual process of re-discovering their true gender identity.

The situation for these adults is very similar to that of teenagers in that this group has a higher than average rate of suicide. In a straw poll survey it has been found that 11 out of 12 people with GID have either attempted to end their own lives or have seriously contemplated doing it. Then there are those who live highly dysfunctional lives because they are forced to live in a constant state of conflict; something they hate doing and from which they long to escape. But they feel unable to disclose their condition, because they are literally terrified of the consequences that will follow, and as we will see later on, it is with very good reason. In this regard they are in much the same situation as the teenagers we mentioned earlier, in that they too feel the same fear and vulnerability. In other words, adults with GID continue to carry the same fears into their adult lives as they have done throughout their childhood and teens. Some of these points are being repeated but it is important for the reader to be aware of how much is at stake and the cost to everyone involved.

This then is the background against which people with GID struggle to cope and against which they must make a decision on whether to seek a diagnosis for their gender conflict. It also affects their decision on whether to proceed with gender reassignment. So no matter how much a person with GID may long to live as normal a life as possible within their true gender, and no matter how much they want to make a disclosure of their diagnosis, the price they are likely to pay in terms of losing family, friends, jobs etc. is just too great. And it is precisely for this reason that so many will opt to stay as they are for as long as they can.

Chapter Five

A BRIEF HISTORY OF GENDER IDENTITY DISORDER IN IRELAND

Life is not always what it seems to be!

It has long been held - wrongly as it happens - that Laurence Michael Dillon was the first Irishman to successfully transition from female to male. In fact Dillon was originally born in London, England. He was born a female and named Laura Maude Dillon, the sister of Sir Robert Dillon, 44, eighth Baronet, of Lismullen in Ireland. It is true that Laurence successfully transitioned from female to male and even managed to have his Birth Certificate amended to reflect his correct gender identity; something that was possible until the Corbett v Corbett case in the UK in 1987.

Between then and now the history of Gender Identity Disorder in Ireland is quite sparse and only serves to reinforce the fact that the condition has been completely hidden for such a very long time. In more recent times there have been a small handful of people who have made their contribution in bringing GID to the fore. The problem with this is that some are not Irish and this has proven to be something of a disadvantage. Also, though their stories were certainly moving and worthy of attention, they persisted in using the old terminologies, which only served to cause a lot of confusion and made it difficult for the general public to make the connection with GID as a clinical condition that affects people in Ireland as well as other countries. The other problem has been the confrontational approach taken under the assumption that the state and health service providers have known about the condition for a long time and simply chose to ignore it. But more recent evidence shows the contrary to be the case. That is not to say that there wasn't some awareness amongst some health service providers, upon which they had failed to act.

The fact remains that the problem of Gender Identity Disorder has been perceived as the problem of people from other countries and not something that occurs in Ireland. Nothing could be further from the truth.

It is important to mention here the people who made their own contributions to raising awareness of Gender Identity Disorder. They have been heroes in their own right and made it possible for the author and one or two other *Irish* people with GID to go public with our condition. One of the very first members of the medical profession to provide a service for people seeking help and diagnosis was the late Dr. Margaret O'Regan, who unfortunately died some years ago as the result of a drowning accident. Margaret was as a psychiatrist and was one of a small handful of psychiatrists who actively treated people with GID and sought to encourage a number of her peers to do likewise, regrettably without much success.

Diane and Caroline Hughes are owed an immense debt of gratitude for their tremendous courage and fortitude in raising the issue of GID for over a decade despite the fact they both come from Wales. This is especially relevant when considering that it would have been so much easier for them to just live quiet lives and avoid the negative comments they were both subjected to over a long period of time, and before

GID was more openly discussed within this country.

Another two people to be mentioned here is Dr Nicholas Krievenko, who along with his wife Sydney has struggled to have the Irish state recognise their marriage, which is recognised in other countries around the world. Dr Krievenko is a female to male and was featured amongst others on the "Big Bite" show in 2004. It was Diane Hughes and Doctor Krievenko who made a significant contribution to the *Nexus Report*, which was commissioned by the Equality Authority and published in 2005.

Dr. Lydia Foy is worthy of mention here as she is unquestionably one of the most public of all Irish people with Gender Identity Disorder. This however was not intentional but rather came about as a result of her case before the High Court being publicised within the national and tabloid media. Her being in the public limelight has been due to her action before the High Court to have her Birth Certificate amended so as to reflect her true gender. It is fair to say that Lydia has dealt with the stress of having her personal life dragged through the media with the utmost dignity, and is an inspiration to all those going through their own personal battles to live in their true gender.

In 2002 the High Court ruled against Lydia's application to have her Birth Certificate amended to reflect her true gender. The case was taken on behalf of Dr Foy by the Free Legal Aid Centre (FLAC), Dublin, who has been steadfast in their determination to see a satisfactory outcome, not just for Lydia, but for all those who seek the right to live in accordance with their true gender identity. What is truly extraordinary about Lydia's case is that just two days after the High Court ruled against her application the European Court of Human Rights ruled against the UK because of its refusal to grant the right of UK citizens with Gender Identity Disorder to amend their Birth certificates. It has taken five years for Lydia's case to go back before the High Court and was once again heard before the same Judge in April 2007.

In October 2007 a judgement was delivered by Judge McKechnie in which he issued a Declaration of Incompatibility against the Irish State. In his judgement, Justice McKechnie made it clear that people with Gender Identity Disorder ought to have their true gender legally recognised and that the Irish government should act immediately in resolving the matter by introducing the appropriate legislation that will afford the legal recognition required and that would then enable people with GID to change their Birth Certificates. As of the date of publication, the High Court Judgement has been appealed by the government to the Supreme Court.

The government's actions in relation to the rights of people with GID have become rather contradictory and bizarre over the past number of years. For example, while the government are opposing the decision in the Dr. Foy case they have enacted the new Passport Act, 2008, which gives legal recognition to the passports of people with GID, who acquired their new passports after changing their name by Deed Poll. This appears to be inconsistent with its other actions given that the issuing of a passport is based on the passport holder's Birth Certificate. There is also recognition of GID as a medical condition within a number of government departments including the Department of Health and Children, the Department of the Environment and the Department of Justice, Equality and Law Reform and the Department of Social and Family Affairs. This situation is patently absurd. It demonstrates the urgent need for a more coherent and structured approach to putting the necessary legislation and other facilities in place that will enable people with GID to alter their Birth certificates and thereby end much of the discrimination experienced by this group.

Also in recent times we saw the first medical symposium to be held in Ireland on Gender Identity Disorder. This event was co-sponsored by the Equality Authority, the Health Service Executive and The Department of Health and Children, with the Minister for Health and Children, Ms Mary Harney TD in attendance. Gender Identity Disorder Ireland (GIDI) and TENI also participated in the working group responsible for the medical symposium and the new treatment pathway. This latter development should not be lost on health service providers across the country. Other developments in this area are the publication of a number of articles on GID within a number of professional medical journals for the health sector and for counsellors and psychotherapist organisations.

There are ongoing developments within the HSE in that a review was undertaken in order to determine what healthcare resources are currently available within the hospital system which can be made accessible to patients seeking treatment. There is also the development of an agreed referral pathway for the various stages of the gender reassignment process, with the various ancillary supports attached, e.g. counselling, therapy etc. These are very welcome developments and in time will prove extremely beneficial to GID patients. So in some respects things are improving and there is every reason to believe they will continue to improve further.

More recently still is the founding of the first registered charity specifically to support people with Gender Identity

Disorder. The name of the organisation is Gender Identity Disorder Ireland (GIDI), which was founded in 2007. It is the first and only organisation within the country which deals with Gender Identity Disorder as an exclusively medical condition. This organisation provides a variety of services which focuses on the issues surrounding GID. Their services are also available to the families, friends etc. of those living with the condition. The organisation also acts in an advisory capacity and has participated in a number of roundtable working groups, e.g. the European Commission's Social Realty Report and the working group for the Third Shadow Report for the United Nations on the International Convention on Civil and Political Rights. In September 2008, the Irish Human Rights Commission (IHRC) issued a submission to the Irish Government on the need to establish a working group to examine law reform on transgendered (GID) rights. This is with a view to the Irish government introducing legislation allowing people with GID to alter their Birth Certificates which will then protect their identities and their right to privacy.

This pretty much brings us up to date, except to say that there are a number of key developments taking place that will go much further in terms of placing Gender Identity Disorder where it belongs within the mainstream of healthcare provision and which will eventually bring into existence the necessary legal recognition that will enable people with GID to alter their Birth certificates and thereby afford them the same civil and human rights enjoyed by the citizens of this country.

Chapter Six

GENDER IDENTITY DISORDER
IN THE MEDIA

Can Irish journalists begin to apply more thought and
consideration to the editorial decisions
they take and the ethical choices they make
in their work?
Damien Kiberd

The role of the media generally in reporting gender
related issues and personal stories is very significant and its
impact on public consciousness has been immense in terms
of the impression it has created of those who struggle with
their condition on a day-to-day basis. The coverage of stories
and issues over the years has been anything from well
informed and sensitively dealt with, to downright offensive
and deeply hurtful. The best that could be said historically
about some of the media's handling of the issues and
personal stories, is that it has been negligent and reckless, not
to forget salacious, sensationalist and misleading. The media
are renowned too for showing little or no regard for the
impact it has on the lives of those who have entrusted their
own personal stories. It is never an easy thing for people with
GID to tell their personal stories through the media; in fact it
takes a great deal of trust and courage to do so. And to be
frank about it, some media have abused the privilege for the
sake of getting a scoop. This kind of bad faith towards their
contributors does nothing to recommend them for future

cooperation. It should also be remembered that these people do not get any form of payment for sharing such deep personal information about their lives.

In far too many instances the media have resorted to salaciousness, sensationalism and downright falsehoods simply in order to get people to buy their papers. This is invariably at the expense of those who contributed their personal stories and of the wider GID population; who often find themselves portrayed as abnormal, sexual deviants and freaks that have something to hide and to be ashamed of. And when the media are confronted with their offences, they quickly resort to abrogating themselves of any moral or ethical responsibility. Some of the excuses offered are of the most superficial kind while others simply don't bother to respond at all. Some promise to put right the offence caused, but they either never do, or, their efforts fall far short of what is required. It will be amply demonstrated as we proceed that the media's behaviour towards GID related issues does have a significant impact. It certainly does affect people's decisions on whether to seek help in the first instance and once diagnosed on whether to proceed with gender reassignment.

Newspapers & Magazines

We will turn our attention firstly to newspapers and magazines in order to demonstrate the worst and the best of how GID issues are still being reported. It will be shown that for the most part the broadsheets tend to better than the tabloids, but surprisingly enough only just!

One quote from an article published in the Sunday Tribune in February 2008 shows the impact that the media's and the general public's fascination has on the lives of people with Gender Identity Disorder and who have the courage to tell their stories. The journalist in question is Sarah McInerney. She was interviewing the author for her new book: *Becoming Myself: The True Story of Thomas Who Became Sara*. The article was a fine piece of journalism and gave an accurate; one might even say a flattering account of the interview and what transpired during it. At the top of the article the journalist relates the story of a conversation she had with her flatmate about the interview she was about to do with a woman who used to be a man. She was then asked a number of typical questions which are often asked about people in this situation. Ms McInerney summarised the conversation quite accurately when she wrote:

> *"The questions kept coming in a lazily fascinated fashion. Innocently ignorant, certainly not meant to be insulting. But for people like Sara Jane Cromwell, every such query is a fresh wound."*

The general public still has a fascination with the various issues surrounding Gender Identity Disorder, albeit under the guise of terms such as Transsexualism, Transgenderism and sex-change surgery. This is entirely understandable. It is also understandable that the media will then want to cover such issues and stories. And it is even understandable that the headlines on printed articles are bound to be sensationalised, to some degree at least, and in such a way as to arouse the reader's interest in the story, but at what price to the article? And at what price to those affected? It is a fact that inappropriate headlines do have an adverse effect not just on the substance of the story or article, but more importantly, on the consciousness of the readers and their understanding of GID. Of course there is also the impact on those who have to live with the fallout produced by these headlines. In order to demonstrate this point I have included here a sample of the kinds of headlines referred to. The headlines listed below are just a sample of the type still in use by the newspaper and magazine media. Here is a small perception test. As you read through these headlines, see if you can accurately tell what these headlines are referring to:

"Why we Chose to Invest in Designer Vaginas"
(Star Sunday)
"I'm Glad I Had a Sex Change"
(Belfast Telegraph)
"Sex Swap is now a Cert" *(Star Sunday)*
"Sex Op Sara's Family Dispute Her Books Claims"
(The Echo, Ballyfermot and Tallaght)
"Wife Booted Me Out When I Became a Woman"
(Star Sunday)
"Family's Fury as Girl, 12, Allowed to Have Sex-Change against Father's Wishes" *(Daily Mail, UK edition).*

How many readers of these headlines would feel even remotely comfortable knowing they were referring to them personally or to one of their family or friends? Yet these are the kinds of salacious and sensationalist headlines that people with GID are confronted with on a regular basis. Space does not permit us to look at all these headlines in detail but we will look at one or two in terms of how they have little or no bearing on the stories themselves, and how they can reinforce the public's lack of understanding and prevents people coming forward medical help.

The first headline we shall look at is the one entitled: *"Why We Chose to Invest in Designer Vaginas"*. This headline accompanied a story about my own and Lynda Sheridan's struggle to become the women we were always meant to be, and the need to bring Gender Identity Disorder into the mainstream. This was done precisely so that people would have a more accurate understanding of the issues surrounding the condition, as well as its impact on the lives of those affected by it. It was made abundantly clear to the journalist concerned that we would not agree to the interview if her newspaper was going to use salacious, sensationalist or inaccurate headlines and that any pictures must be appropriate and in good taste. Having been given these assurances we proceeded with the interview. We went to great pains to point out that GID has nothing whatsoever to do with transvestism, crossdressing or sexuality. It was further pointed out, that terms such as *Transsexualism* and *Transgenderism* are also inappropriate and no longer recognised by many in the medical profession.

When the article was published with the above headline there was great hurt and offence. To make matters even worse (as if they could be) there was a picture of three transvestites, which clearly associated us with them, but which had absolutely no relevance to the article or our reasons for doing it. When the newspaper was challenged about this they tried to justify it on the grounds that the headline came from something my former colleague had said during the interview. It had to do with a quip made by her surgeon while she was in hospital for her genital realignment surgery. The decision to use the headline was made by one of the papers sub-editors, despite the fact that it had absolutely nothing to do with the article itself and was bound to detract from the substance of what the article was trying to achieve. What also made this headline and its implications so offensive was the fact that I had not completed my own reassignment process and had not yet completed my GRS.

This headline and its inferences where a gross invasion not only of my own privacy, but also of those who have or will one day go through this surgical procedure; in that it completely trivialises an extremely serious medical issue. However what was probably most offensive and hurtful was the way in which the headline completely trivialised what is a very serious and dangerous surgical procedure which patients would certainly not undertake, unless it was absolutely necessary. Later on we will look at some of the effects these types of headlines can have on the public's perception of GID, and realignment surgery in particular. What was especially disappointing about this headline is the way in which it completely undermined what was actually a very good article indeed.

The next example to look at is the 12 year old girl who was the subject of the following headline: *"Family's Fury as Girl, 12, Allowed to Have Sex-Change against Father's Wishes"* This headline is damning in so far as it gives the impression that this young twelve year old girl is having a *sex-change,* when that actually was not the case at all. The facts about this story are that the child has identified as a boy from a very young age and nothing could be done to make her think otherwise. As she reached pubescence her sense of being a male in the wrong body has grown, to the point where she is at serious risk of self-harming. This is because she is unable to cope with puberty and developing a teenage girl's body. This is a classic case of young gender dysphoric female to male struggling with their gender identity. To complicate matters for this young girl, her parents are separated and there is clearly a great deal of animosity between them, which is affecting their daughter's own struggles. Her father had opposed her wishes to begin hormone treatment at the earliest opportunity. The hormone treatment is vitally important in that it will prevent her from developing breasts and other physical characteristics which are typical for a teenage girl. Her mother on the other hand is fully supportive of her wishes to begin transitioning towards developing a male body.

However, in order to do this, the mother had to apply to the courts for a judgement that would allow her daughter to proceed with her hormone treatment. Having weighed up all the evidence the judge in the case deemed it *essential* that the girl begin hormone treatment at the earliest opportunity. Now here's the point; the hormone treatment is reversible up to about 16 years of age and there are at least two landmark stages during the transition process which allows the girl to revert back if she so chooses. Not only this, she must return to court seeking further orders for the latter stages of the reassignment process. This is a legal requirement until the girl reaches 18 years of age, which is the age of consent. In the meantime she will be allowed to change her Birth Certificate, Passport and her Medicare card into a boy's name.

Another key problem with this article is that the *facts* of the case are sandwiched between the unqualified opinions and comments of two individuals who have nothing to do with the case. One is the girl's cousin, who makes no effort to hide her animosity towards the girl's mother (if she is being quoted accurately). The other person is a Roman Catholic professor in bioethics, who also has nothing to do with the case. Yet he is able to express some extremely presumptuous and inflammatory opinions on the young girl's situation, and seemingly without any regard for the extensive and drawn out assessment process that goes with a diagnosis of Gender Identity Disorder. It is quite clear from his comments that he has no real understanding of the clinical nature of this condition and the impact it has on the lives of those affected by it. His knowledge of the subject seems to be wholly academic erroneous and without any clinical expertise whatsoever. But this unfortunately does not prevent such individuals from expressing opinions about issues for which they have little understanding, and without any regard for the harm they cause.

It is precisely this kind of selective and irresponsible reporting that negatively impacts on the public's consciousness and which in turn affects their perceptions and attitudes on these issues. This is an extremely important concern for those parents whose children are already showing character traits that are consistent with Gender Identity Disorder. In light of the impact that these articles can have, what is the likelihood of these parents having their children properly assessed for the condition; even if it is to eliminate the possibility and so dispel their fears? The answer is: very slim indeed. The ultimate effect of this is that those children will be condemned to face a hellish future in which none of these journalists and those influenced by them will be seen. They will have done their work and moved on to their next story.

On the plus side there is evidence that more journalists are taking the issues around GID more seriously and are less likely to write in the manner outlined above. This is a welcome development. However there is still the problem of the sub-editors who behave as a law unto themselves and have little regard for either the nature or the substance of the articles for which they write headlines. Nor do they show much regard for the contributors who are most likely to be affected by the way they present their stories. Whilst this is clearly not true of all editors and sub-editors, it is true for too many of them.

Of course a big part of the problem with being published in any of the printed media is that the contributor has absolutely no control over what is published after they have finished their interview. And it is not always possible to rely upon the assurances given by the journalists conducting the interviews, even if they mean well. The simple fact is that once any article or interview has been submitted, it is then down to the editors and sub-editors to decide what gets published; how much of it gets published; what is the particular slant they wish to use and the response or reaction they are trying to provoke. The impact on the contributors, their personal feelings and any wider implications from the published article tends not to be that important a consideration. And if the contributor deigns to make a complaint, well the editors can always abrogate their responsibilities by referring to the *freedom of the press.*

It is commendable though, that even the Irish tabloid media have *started* to get to grips with the tragedy that is Gender Identity Disorder and they are to be commended for the way in which they have begun to report the condition more accurately and to narrate individual stories in a far more sensitive manner. However this is in no small part due to the sterling and persistent work being done by Gender Identity Disorder Ireland (GIDI) and its work in raising awareness regarding the true clinical nature of the condition.

While it is deeply gratifying to see a much improved standard of reporting on GID, there is no cause for complacency. The newspaper and magazine media must continue to improve the manner in which they report on these sensitive issues and remember that they are dealing with issues that can deeply impact upon people's lives.

Television and Radio

Now we will turn our attention to radio and television, which it has to be said tends to fair better than the printed media when it comes to reporting on GID related issues. There are of course the obvious exceptions such as Jerry Springer, Ricky Lake, Maury etc. in the US, while in the UK there are the daytime talk shows. But they by and large don't deal with issues such as GID in quite the same way as those just mentioned from the US. It is highly regrettable that the first contact Irish people have had with GID is through such crude and distasteful programmes. These programmes reinforce the need for all forms of media in this country to be as ethical and sensitive as possible when reporting on issues relating to GID.

It is to the credit of all four Irish TV broadcasters that, for the most part at least, they do not engage in the kind of salacious and frivolous reporting of issues and stories relating to GID. This can also be said of the numerous radio broadcasters around the country. Having said this, the one criticism that could be made against them is that they don't cover the topic anywhere near enough. This is especially true of local radio where a great deal of good could result from covering the issue. After all it is within the local community that every person living with GID seeks to live out their lives, which makes them no different from anyone else with the same aspiration. The reality is that there needs to be greater coverage of the issue, which can help significantly in the normalisation of people with the condition. The television media could do more work in this area, which in itself would be a major positive contribution to the issue.

The signs that the television media were ready to embrace the subject of GID and gender reassignment in particular, insofar as it affected Irish people specifically, started in November of 2004, when The Big Bite Show brought the issues of GID into the public domain in a way that was fundamentally different from anything that had occurred heretofore, in that it dealt with the problems of Irish people living with Gender Identity Disorder. It was no longer a case of dismissing people with GID as the kind of psychologically disturbed attention seeking freaks who appear on the type of American programmes mentioned earlier.

This was followed by the reporting of the Lydia Foy case in the High Court in which Ms Foy sought to have her birth certificate changed so as to reflect her true gender and sex following her genital realignment surgery. Then the Late Late Show had a number of guests on who were able to tell their stories of struggling with life in the wrong body and all that that entailed; I was the most recent to be interviewed following the publication of my first book. TV3 have also interviewed a number of people with GID and they too are to be commended for the professional manner in which they conducted their interviews. That said, it was also clear from these interviews that the interviewers were not always as well informed as they might have been.

There is one radio broadcast in particular that stands out for its unprofessional, reckless and irresponsible interviewing techniques. It was a Dublin based radio station and the interview was about the publication of the same book mentioned earlier. The reason for mentioning this interview here is because it links into what was said before about the impact the newspaper media can have on the public's consciousness and from this the public's attitude towards GID issues and genital realignment surgery in particular. My understanding was that the interview was about my book and nothing else, and coming as I was from doing numerous other interviews for the book, I was not mentally prepared to answer any questions about the broader issues surrounding GID. As I waited to be interviewed I was told that there would be a vox-pop just before I went live on air. I was not told about the nature of the vox pop.

The question in the vox pop that was put to members of the public was: *should taxpayers be expected to pay for sex-changes?* It was quite obvious that the people who responded knew very little if anything about Gender Identity Disorder as a clinical condition, with many being under the impression that gender realignment surgery (sex-change) was nothing more than a lifestyle choice. It was no surprise then to find most of those questioned being against taxpayers paying for this type of surgery. To say I was annoyed would be an understatement and I was strongly tempted to pull out of the interview altogether. However I went ahead with it and dealt with the issue head on, which as it happened turned out to be quite positive in the end, as listeners very quickly realised the true nature of the condition and why it is that genital realignment surgery along with the changing of the Birth Certificate are so vital to the outcome of the reassignment process.

It is at this point that a fundamental difference exists between radio and television interviews on the one hand and printed interviews on the other. As mentioned earlier, the contributors to printed interviews have absolutely no control over what is actually published, whereas those involved in live interviews do; whether it is by television or radio. How they get on is another matter altogether, but at least they are in control of what they say and to some extent at least, can influence the subsequent reactions from those watching and listening.

From everything that has been said thus far, it should be obvious that the media as a whole has a very significant role to play in how issues relating to GID are reported and portrayed before the public. It has been amply demonstrated that both the content and the manner in which information is conveyed to the public can and does have a significant impact upon the public's consciousness and that this in turn affects their perceptions and attitudes. We saw how the misreporting of issues relating to GID can have a very negative impact on those who struggle with the condition and how it affects their decision to seek help and whether they should go through the reassignment process or continue to live with the condition; as intolerable as that is.

We also looked at the consequences for parents who believe their children may have the character traits that would indicate at least the possibility that their child may have the condition. The point was made that some of these parents may think twice about taking their child to be assessed, especially after having read or listened to so much negative and misleading information about GID, and the reassignment process in particular. This would undoubtedly be a great tragedy and it is certain that in a significant number of cases also lead to the tragic loss of young lives.

As the vox pop also demonstrated, the impact of the media's coverage of issues such as GID can affect whether or not people feel that genital realignment surgery should be paid for by taxpayers. This too can have the negative impact just mentioned and indeed it already does with higher than average numbers considering or attempting to end their lives by suicide, rather than feel forced to go on living a false life. And when they do take that most tragic of steps, there are sure to be no journalists around to pick up the pieces and make things better.

Chapter Seven

LIVING THE REAL LIFE EXPERIENCE IN IRELAND

This above all, to thine own self be true,
And it must follow, as the night the day,
Thou canst not then be false to any man.

Shakespeare

Changing Gender Role

Once a decision has been made to proceed with Gender Reassignment, the patient is required to go through a transitional phase known as the Real Life Experience (Test). The period normally lasts for about two years from the time of starting life in the new social gender role to Genital Realignment Surgery. There is a mind-numbing array of challenges that have to be undertaken and many difficult experiences in order to live within one's true gender identity. To say that it is a stressful path to walk would be a major understatement. What is probably the most difficult aspect of their reassignment is the isolation. It truly is a most lonely process to go through with no guarantee of a positive outcome. What follows is a number of the major issues and problems that have to be dealt with in order to make a successful transition.

Changing Legal Identity

Apart from the medical and physical changes that must

occur in order to complete transition, another important issue that needs to be addressed is taking a new name. Many GID people pick their own names, while others may have them suggested for them. In order for a name change to have legal effect it must be changed by Deed Poll. A sworn declaration must be made and sent to the High Court. The declaration must contain both the old name and the new name to be used once the Deed Poll is authorised. Once the Deed Poll has been completed by the High Court the individual must henceforth be known only by that name.

All legal and other documentation must be changed to the new name. This can be quite complicated and drawn out, especially when having to deal with authorities, insurance company's etc., who can sometimes prove to be less than understanding. This can only add to the distress and humiliation already experienced.

Changing Documents

Those individuals going through the real life experience can change all their legal documents, except their Birth Certificates, e.g. passports, academic accreditations etc. All legal documents, especially passport and driving licences etc., are based upon the Birth Certificate; yet they are unable to alter this document at the present time. Below is a list of just some of the documents that must be changed following the completion of the Deed Poll:

- Passport
- Driving Licence
- Car Tax & Insurance
- Life Assurance
- Bank Accounts

- Credit Cards
- Credit Union
- Wills
- Accreditations, e.g. Degrees, Diplomas etc.
- Business Documentation, e.g. Business Cards etc.

It can be nerve-wrecking having to go and tell your bank, licensing authorities etc. that your name has been changed by Deed Poll and that you not only require a change of name on your documentation, but that you are changing from a male to a female name and that you want to have your correct gender indicated on the documents. Sometimes this is *not* done and there is contradictory information regarding the holder's gender identity entered into their files. This issue amounts to discrimination a denial of the individual's right to privacy, which is something cherished by every other citizen.

At the time of writing, the only document that cannot be changed is the Birth Certificate. This is a major drawback for people with GID and has a very significant impact upon their ability to live their lives fully within their true identity. This is because every other document is derived from the gender assigned to them on their Birth Certificate and this is absolutely fundamental to who and what they are in terms of their true gender. Ireland is in the bottom three of forty countries within the Council of Europe who deny people the right to change their name and gender on Birth Certificates. The failure of the Irish state to provide people with GID the right to alter their Birth Certificates exposes such people to all manner of discrimination whether deliberate or otherwise and has been ruled as a violation of their human rights under Articles 8 and 12 of the ECHR Act, 2003.

Not having the proper Birth Certificate can affect a patient's admittance to hospital and what ward they will be allocated to, i.e. male or female. The birth Certificate affects life assurance and motor insurance cover premiums. These are extremely serious issues and they need to be addressed by the state as humanely as possible. The fact is that most if not all these and other problems would disappear were appropriate legislation introduced, which would give legal recognition to people with GID and afford them the legal right to alter their Birth certificates; thereby securing for them the same right to privacy guaranteed to every Irish citizen under our Constitution.

One of the sobering facts in all of this is that even in countries such as Iran, people with GID are legally recognised and have access to all the health care they need in order to successfully complete their gender reassignment.

Presentation

There are other problems that have to be addressed if the person with GID is to integrate within society. Major issues to do with how they dress, walk, talk, sit stand and where to put their hands, are all issues they have to take on board. In other words, how passable are they once they start their real life experience? The whole experience can leave them feeling extremely self-conscious and vulnerable, and can be the difference between success and failure, between being *passable* and being *spotted (read)*; something that terrifies each one. Most male-to-female women are completely clueless when it comes to knowing how to be as passable as possible. It is unfortunately true that many dress in a manner that is completely inappropriate and as a result draws the wrong kind of attention. There is no point in denying that many do dress and look like transvestites. This is in part because they are over-compensating for their masculine features. It is though mainly because they are totally alone when going through transition and are genuinely frightened to ask for help. It has to be said though, that in some cases there are those individuals who will neither seek nor accept help of any kind, which can lead to negative reactions from families, friends and the general public.

For many it is as basic as trying to find the right shoes and clothes. To do this some resort to going to charity shops, while others will buy online, or get a sympathetic friend to help them. Many are frightened at the prospects of using female or male changing rooms. Once the various items have been purchased the next challenge is where to keep them. This is exceptionally difficult where the spouse and children are unsupportive or where they have not yet been informed of the situation. This is where the idea of living the double-life starts to manifest itself; there is the constant fear of their clothes and makeup being discovered. In such circumstances there is the added problem of accusations of being a transvestite and that this is really all about sex and not to do with gender identity. This is why it is imperative that everyone who is diagnosed with GID should inform their loved ones at the earliest opportunity. There is understandably reluctance amongst some, due to the price they expect to pay if they do make a disclosure. However, as difficult as this will be, the problem of leaving it and creating an atmosphere of suspicion and distrust will exact a much higher price.

Completing the Deed Poll is essential if they are to transition successfully, especially during the early stages were there has been little change to their facial appearance apart from wearing makeup etc. It is especially important in situations where they have to use public facilities and where there is a risk of being *discovered*. These individuals need to have some kind of identification to confirm that they are who they claim to be, and more importantly, that they are the appropriate gender for the facilities they are using. This is far more difficult for male-to-female than female-to-male. For example, using the ladies toilets and ladies dressing rooms can be an absolutely terrifying ordeal and has the potential to cause terrible humiliation for those who are *spotted*. Shopping is therefore a very stressful experience and it takes a very long time before the person can feel comfortable going into public places. They become preoccupied with other people looking at them and nearly always assume that those people have twigged something! Some do and can react in a number of ways, from mild curiosity to outright ridicule and aggression. For example, there was the case of a person with GID using the women's toilets in a well known shopping centre in Cork who was mistaken for a man. Some of the customers using the toilets insisted she leave and called on security to have her removed. Unfortunately for the individual concerned she had no matching identification which of course made the situation so much worse and humiliating for her. It is precisely in order to minimise the risk of these situations arising that those with GID, who opt for gender reassignment, ensure that they have all the necessary identification in place *before* they start going out in public.

Problems with Identification

It is hard to overstate the numerous opportunities there are for people with GID to experience humiliation, especially in situations involving conflicting identifications. For example those who are just starting the transition stage of their gender reassignment and who have not yet changed their name by Deed Poll and where they still use their original forms of identification. One of the most frightening experiences to be faced is an encounter with the Gardaí; situations involving being stopped and having to provide some form of identification, e.g. driving licence etc., but where this identification does not match the individuals physical appearance, e.g. where the documents identify the individual as male but they present as female. The individual must then try to explain their situation and hope that the Gardaí are enlightened enough or informed enough to handle the situation with sensitivity and due courtesy. There is an argument to be made for ensuring that the Gardaí are sufficiently trained, or at least sufficiently informed of their duties in relation to how they interact with people in these situations. This is similarly the case with the emergency services and the Civil Defence, for example.

There is a special difficulty involving stop and search, or where an individual is taken into custody and where a search and detention is involved. A particular problem arises when a decision must be made as to where the person is to be detained. As at the time of publication these issues have still not been properly addressed. A person who is placed in detention or brought before the courts is identified and presented on the basis of their birth certificate and not their physical appearance. It is not hard to imagine therefore the opportunity for utter humiliation and other consequent difficulties for the individual concerned. This problem extends to courts and prisons etc.

There is real potential for the denial of a person's civil and human rights where they are not afforded the legal protection of the state and where they are not allowed to alter their birth certificates to recognise their *clinically* diagnosed gender identity.

Try to imagine a situation in which a person appears before the courts as a female but is constantly referred to in their male name, or situations requiring a full body search by a female Garda and vice versa. This is so utterly humiliating that it doesn't bare thinking about. This is a very real and significant issue and needs to be addressed by the relevant government departments and the Garda Síochána. It is vital that appropriate operational policies and procedures are put in place to manage such situations. This is vital if the human and civil rights of people with GID are to be protected and where their personal dignity is to remain intact. This requires An Garda Síochána engaging with the subject of Gender Identity Disorder and including it in its training syllabus. There also needs to be a greater face-to-face interaction between the Gardaí and those working in the area of support for people with GID.

Another situation with the potential for humiliation is interactions between people with GID and the emergency services, including admission to hospital. Should a patient be admitted to a male or female ward? This is a question that is usually unnecessary, but not so in the case of people with GID who are still going through their transition or in some cases even when they have completed their GRS. Hospital staff, who have not yet received adequate training in this area, run the risk of seriously mishandling such situations, These situations require understanding and the utmost sensitivity. It is vital therefore that the HSE engages with this

ADDENDUM TO PAGES 101-107

Following the original publication of this book the Irish Government withdrew its appeal to the Supreme Court in the Lydia Foy case.

They established a Gender Recognition Advisory Group under the Department of Social Protection. The purpose for establishing the Advisory Group was to advise the Government on how to proceed in introducing appropriate legislation on Gender Recognition.

The Advisory Group has completed it's consultations and presented its report to the Minister of Social Protection. The Government have accepted the GRAG Report and the Legislation is currently being drafted.

issue and that they develop a policy for the appropriate and sensitive management of patients who present with GID.

The Role of the State

Before going any further, it should be said from the outset, that the state has a legitimate right and obligation to protect the rights of those spouses and children who are likely to be adversely affected by the altering of the Birth Certificate of the other spouse or parent with GID. This is because there would be effectively a same sex marriage, for which there is currently no provision in Irish law. And there must be a legal remedy for those spouses who opt not to remain within a marriage where the other spouse has changed gender roles. None of this however addresses the rights of those who have been diagnosed with Gender Identity Disorder and who have followed the prescribed treatment process and completed their gender reassignment, including genital realignment surgery.

The States Obligations

The Irish State, as represented by our government, not only has a moral responsibility but it also has a constitutional obligation to protect the rights of its citizens. This obligation is enshrined within **Articles 40:1** and **40:3.1⁰** respectively of the Constitution. These Articles state:

"All citizens shall, as human persons,
be equal before the law."
"This shall not be held to mean that the
state shall not in its enactments have
due regard to differences of capacity,

101

physical and moral, and of social function."

And

"The state guarantees in its laws to respect and as far as practicable, by its laws to defend and vindicate the personal rights of the citizen."
"The state shall in particular by its laws protect as best it may from unjust attack and, in the case of injustice done, vindicate the life, person, good name and property rights of every citizen."

Yet in the case of people with Gender Identity Disorder and their affected ability to *function equally* and normally within society, the Irish government are failing and are therefore in breach of its constitutional and human rights obligations to enact laws that will give these citizens their due recognition and protection. To the author's knowledge there is currently only one piece of legislation on the Irish Statute Book that gives any specific form of legal right to Irish citizens with GID, and that is the Passport Act, 2008. Other rights, such as equality are covered but not necessarily specifically stated, e.g. the **Equal Status Act** and the **Employment Equality Act.**

Further to this are the Irish government's obligations under **Articles 8** and **12** of the ECHR, which was ratified by Ireland in 1953, but was not enacted into Irish law until 2003. Ireland also has obligations under **Articles 16** and **26** respectively of the **International Covenant on Civil and Political Rights,** which Ireland ratified in 1990. As mentioned earlier, Ireland is in the bottom three countries within the Council of Europe not to afford legal recognition and protection for people with Gender Identity Disorder. The other two countries are Albania and Andorra!

In October 2007, Justice McKechnie of the High Court issued a judgment in favour of Dr Lydia Foy's application for a Declaration of Incompatibility against the Irish state, under Articles 8 and 12 of the EHCR. He subsequently issued the Declaration, but it has been appealed by the government to the Supreme Court. This is a highly regressive step on the part of our government, and it is one which is causing deep despair among those whose hopes were raised following the initial judgement. What the government and all those who take a facile approach to this issue fail to realise is, that what we are dealing with here is an extraordinary human tragedy, which deserves to be treated as more than just an academic point of law or a cause for frivolous comments and legal opinions.

An Irish citizen's Birth Certificate is their most fundamental form of legal identity and recognition within this state. The individual citizens' ability to function *equally* and *normally* within their daily lives is fundamentally dependent upon this primary legal document and all other legal documents are based upon the contents of this one Certificate. Yet citizens of this country, whose true genders are medically diagnosed as being in conflict with those stated on their Birth certificates, are denied the right to alter or correct those same certificates so as to accurately and legally reflect their true gender. This has already been deemed by the European Court of Human Rights (ECHR) to be a violation of these citizen's human rights, insofar as it ruled against the UK because of their failure to provide the appropriate legislation. The UN Committee of Human

Rights has also given this matter their particular attention during the UNCHR hearings in Geneva in July of 2008. None of this is flattering to Ireland and shows us to be a backward state in the way we treat people with GID. The UNCHR has since issued a recommendation to the Irish government:

The State party should also recognise the right of transgender persons to a change of gender by permitting the issuance of new birth certificates.[20]

The argument most used against allowing people with GID to change their Birth Certificates is the negative impact it would have on current marital and familial relationships and that the *status quo* should be maintained; even where there is a clear violation of the minority group's rights. It is to be regretted that this is a view shared by others, including members of the legislature, media, churches etc. However what all these promoters of the status quo fail to realise is, that altering Birth Certificates in this particular situation is not done on a whim nor is it to violate the rights of others. It is borne out of the need to bring one's body and identification into line with one's *true* (internal) *gender identity*. The issuing of a new Birth Certificate is therefore fundamental to the successful completion of this *prescribed* process. And as will be demonstrated later on, the family law as it presently stands already provides a number of remedies that will afford the necessary protection to spouses and children's property and hereditary rights in the event of a marital breakdown due to a spouse or parent opting to go through with gender reassignment.

There is a major oversight in the whole debate about the rights of people with GID versus the rights of those families whose own legal rights may be adversely affected by the introduction of appropriate gender recognition legislation.

This oversight relates to those people with GID who wish to remain single but who are also denied the right to alter their Birth Certificates. The focus has been so much on married individuals that we have lost sight of a significant population of people with GID who either have no wish to marry at present or who may want to, but won't on account of their current situation. And should these same individuals change their minds at a later date then they will simply be bound by the same family law that is currently on our statute books. They would therefore be no worse off than those seeking legal redress through the introduction of Civil Partnership Legislation. The continuing failure to correct the current legal morass will also affect those children and teenagers who are diagnosed at a much younger age. Their right to a normal and dignified life should not be precluded from consideration of how appropriate legislation may be introduced.

The UK government along with many other countries around the world have already managed to resolve these issues through the introduction of appropriate legislation. There is therefore no valid reason or excuse for the continued failure to act in this area. And it is not as if there is not already some precedent for bringing in the necessary legislation into being. We already have within this country and across government departments a series of inconsistencies between the rights of individuals to change their gender identity on their legal documents. The effect of this is that it places these individuals in a legal limbo.

The obvious question that will be asked here by those opposed to the altering of the birth certificate and who cite the individual's ability to change all their other documentation, is: *well if this is the case, why do they need to change their birth certificates?* The answer is quite simple: our birth certificates are the most fundamental of all the legal forms of identification which we possess. It states not just who we are but *what* we are. It means the protection of their privacy, which is the same right enjoyed by every other Irish citizen. It means not being discriminated against and being humiliated in certain situations in which our Birth Certificates are the only acceptable form of identification. The question raised is though rather facetious and betrays a lack of genuine engagement by those asking it. But as the question has been raised let's not be afraid to answer it. This is easily done by posing the following statement: *"you try living with the wrong Birth Certificate and see how long you will wait before trying to have it corrected."*

Another response might be: that *you should try being admitted to hospital and placed in the wrong ward; being stopped by the Gardaí and searched or being placed in detention and body searched; using public facilities such as dressing rooms and toilets and being assessed for insurance purposes.* In other words there are ample opportunities for discrimination and humiliation, in any and every situation where it is required to produce our Birth Certificates. No one should have to suffer any of these experiences simply for the want of issuing a more accurate Birth Certificate.

Apart from all the arguments on both sides of the debate, there is still yet another more compelling reason for bringing in laws that will give legal recognition for people with GID. It is the need to prevent these very problems from arising in the future; thus affecting future generations of people with GID. By providing a legal remedy now it will be possible to prevent future generations of Irish children being condemned to the same fate. They will have a much greater chance at early diagnosis and appropriate treatment, and as a consequence, will be able to avoid the same dilemmas faced by this current generation who find themselves in a legal limbo. In light of the significant developments outlined above, any further objections to introducing the appropriate gender recognition legislation into Ireland, becomes increasingly untenable.

The Role of Religion

It may come as a surprise to some, but a great many people going through gender reassignment want to continue practicing their religion, but are barred from doing so due to the position taken by their respective churches. It has to be said that the majority of religions demonstrate an alarming degree of ignorance of the scientific evidence for Gender Identity Disorder and are even worse when it comes to making moral judgements about those who are diagnosed with it.

It is extremely unfortunate that many of those people with GID who wish to continue practicing their particular religion have to deal head-on with moralising religionists who do nothing but cause a great deal of hurt and distress by their ill-informed views on Gender Identity Disorder. They can be quite forthright in making moralistic judgements and pronouncements against those who struggle with their condition. They are often arrogant and condescending and completely lacking in understanding or compassion. The positions taken by most of these religious organisations are often without the slightest regard for the medical facts, nd where they do take account of the evidence, they are quite dismissive of anything that exposes the weakness of their own position.

An example of this wilful ignorance is the Catholic Church's position on GID, and Genital Realignment Surgery in particular. They hold–despite all the evidence to the contrary, and the position of the World Health Organisation and other distinguished authorities–that a person's gender does not change after they have had GRS. In doing this they completely miss the point and the basis for the surgery being carried out in the first instance. They have gone so far as to write to churches informing them that they are *not* to alter Baptismal Certificates for those Catholic's who have had Gender Realignment Surgery. Needless to say the impact of this position has been quite devastating for many Roman Catholics who wish to continue practicing their faith, but now find themselves in a religious limbo.

There are also cases of Catholic-run hospitals that discriminate against people with GID by refusing to carry out certain GID related surgeries. There are cases of hospitals refusing to perform GRS surgeries, only to change their position when lawsuits are taken out against them. One example of this was reported by the Catholic News Agency, and centres around the case of Charlene Hastings, a 57 year old GID patient, and a Roman Catholic, who was seeking breast augmentation as part of her gender reassignment. The hospital had been previously taken over by the order of the Sisters of Charity, who changed the hospitals policy in relation to Gender Reassignment Surgery. These surgeries were being carried out until the takeover by the religious order. When Ms Hastings enquired about the surgery, she was told she could not have it on religious grounds.[21] However the hospital changed its position following a lawsuit issued against them by Ms Hastings. They also apologised to her for what was termed as *"any confusion that may have come from this situation."* [22] The problem with this kind of volte-face action is that it merely adds to the confusion and distress that the Roman Catholic Church's stance has and is causing for its own loyal members.

Evangelical Christian's do not differ from the Roman Catholic Church on this issue and demonstrate the same lack of understanding and compassion. Instead they demonstrate an equal degree of ignorance and arrogance. Their ignorance of the scientific evidence for GID, and their highly selective misuse of Scripture to justify their position simply beggars belief.

The following quote from the Christian Institute clearly demonstrates the kind of ignorance and misinformation I'm referring to: *The problem, however, is psychological: the evidence supports this view overwhelmingly. The transsexual's body is healthy. Traditionally invasive surgery has only been used to preserve the integrity of a body endangered by disease or injury not to mutilate a healthy body. A painful operation cannot solve the mental disfunction.* [23]

Many of these groups force their own erroneous interpretations of certain Bible verses onto the issue and fail to pay a blind bit of notice to the damage they do in the process. The verse most often quoted in this regard is Deuteronomy 22:5. This verse prohibits Israelite men from wearing female clothing and vice-versa. This verse is taken completely out of context and has absolutely nothing to do with Gender Identity Disorder. On the contrary, it is taken from the Old Testament Law and is part of a long list of prohibitions handed down by Moses to the people of Israel before they entered the Promised Land. The entire book of Deuteronomy is written for this purpose and relates to the people of Israel. What Evangelicals and others do is put these

Old Testament laws onto Christians, while at the same time stating that the Old Testament law was fulfilled in Jesus Christ. It therefore follows that New Testament believers are not bound by these laws. But that is really beside the point. The fact is that the passage concerned has nothing whatever to do with Gender Identity Disorder.

But they don't stop there. They go on to state the following: 1 Corinthians 6:18-20 warns against 'sinning sexually against your own body'. Christians must honour God with their body.[24]

There is really only one word for this: unacceptable. And I say this as a Christian. Again it must be pointed out that this passage has absolutely nothing to do with GID. It is exactly this selective misuse of Scripture that does so much harm to vulnerable and unsuspecting believers. But then, there has always been a multiplicity of double-thinking amongst religionists when it comes to matters of science and medicine not fitting in with their religious thinking and dogma. The impact of this kind of misappropriation of the Bible does the churches no credit and only serves to alienate a significant number of people with GID, who are professing Christians. But because of the attitudes and actions of the churches they are left with nowhere to go and in many cases some do end up leaving the church and end up living on the fringes. They are therefore barred from receiving any form of spiritual support and counselling from their respective religious communities. They are left to deal with their condition alone and disillusioned. Some of the individuals affected in this way have been faithful to their churches and to practicing their beliefs, only now to find themselves completely cut off. The author is personally aware of some of these individuals who after being refused baptism within their own denominations under their new name and gender identity, sought to be baptised into another denomination, where they were accepted with open arms.

All religious organisations need to understand that Gender Identity Disorder is a congenital and neurobiological condition for which there is no known cure. It is *not* a psychological disorder as claimed by some, nor is it a mental illness, nor is it a mere erroneous belief of being born into the wrong body, as some would have us believe. These assertions act as a slight against the good and responsible work of highly responsible and highly reputable professionals who are experts in the field of gender identity and intersex conditions.

The reality is that GID can only be effectively treated through *partial* gender reassignment for some and *full* gender reassignment for others. This is important given the fact that such individuals are acting upon a prescribed treatment from competent practitioners in the fields of psychology, psychiatry and endocrinology. The churches treat people with Gender Identity Disorder as if they could just repent of their decision to have gender reassignment, and then have the condition counselled and prayed out of existence, which is of course patently absurd. This is due in part to the way they select their evidence, which will invariably confirm their own preferred positions. Virtually every religion does this until they are *compelled* to accept otherwise.

The various religions are far too quick to judge and condemn those who change their gender roles. They too often and erroneously assume that the change in gender role is merely a matter of making a sinful and misguided choice. It should be quite obvious by now that this is simply not the case. And it is no coincidence therefore that the clergy and the religious organisations generally figure very poorly when it comes to whom people with GID will turn to when they are depressed and suicidal. It *is not* to the churches.

The various religions should also recognise that they have no business interfering with the treatment paths chosen by those diagnosed with the condition. They should also realise that the condition has nothing whatever to do with the moral or spiritual standing of the individuals concerned. There is however a moral and spiritual imperative for all religions to acquaint themselves properly with the scientific and medical facts behind this condition and to adopt appropriate spiritual and community supports for those who wish to continue fellowshipping with their fellow believers. This *is* the *moral and Christ-like* thing to do.

Chapter Eight

DISCLOSING GENDER IDENTITY DISORDER

*Trust demands a response; the problem is
what kind of response will it be?*

A number of important issues should be addressed before any disclosure of a diagnosis of GID is made. One of the main problems with making a disclosure of this condition is that the person doing it is too often ill-prepared for the task. Another problem is that they are more likely to make the disclosure without any input from outside support services. For example, consultants, local general practitioners and counsellors all have a very significant role to play in how their patients make a disclosure along with the timing of such a disclosure. Having a professional input will not only help the patient making the disclosure, but it can also be an immense help to spouses, partners, children etc. who have to come to terms with such a difficult and life changing announcement. It is very unfortunate that the vast majority do not consider this option. So what are the specific benefits of having a professional intervention while making a disclosure of GID?

- First and foremost, it keeps GID on a medical level where it belongs.

- Second, it means families receiving more factual information about GID than would otherwise be the case.

- Third, it means that families of people with
  GID will have some of the support they need
  in order to come to terms with what is after
  all, a life changing situation for all concerned.

Another major problem with making a disclosure is the way in which it is explained to others. For example those who try to explain their condition with the phrase:, I want to become a woman? and other similar statements create the wrong impression completely. This is because people with GID do not choose their gender, anymore than anyone else chooses to be born male or female. But unfortunately for them and everyone else, using that phrase conveys the idea of someone wanting to change sex and not as it is, a congenital condition. What they really mean is: I want my body to match my female gender identity. It needs to be said that people with GID often confuse the issues for their own families, friends etc., by using confusing and inappropriate language. They also don't help by their own ambivalence towards changing their social gender roles and whether to go through full gender reassignment. People are entitled to be confused by this. This will not be a popular thing to say, especially as it comes from one who is in a similar situation, but it does need to be said nonetheless. This is in recognition of the rights of families to know where they stand in regards to the decisions being made by a spouse or parent.

Meeting the Family, Friends and Work Colleagues

This may seem like a strange heading but it is a very accurate one, because in its fullest sense, this is what is happening when a person with GID enters into their new social gender role. It is completely different to the gender role in which people have been relating to up this point, and for many that is not an easy situation to deal with. There is no escaping the enormity of this for those who are faced with it. However, it is equally impossible to overstate the enormity of the pressure on the person who is introducing themselves in their new gender role. It is almost impossible to overstress the difference that positive and negative reactions can have in how these situations are dealt with. In some cases it is the difference between life and death. It is an extremely difficult and emotional task to undertake, especially where there is a marriage and children involved.

It is fair to say, there can be a significant lack of effort on the part of most to demonstrate any kind of understanding, compassion and acceptance; certainly not in the immediate period after an introduction has taken place. What makes this even more distressing is that these people are their family, friends and work colleagues in whom they have placed so much hope and trust. The anecdotal evidence to date is really quite depressing in terms of the consistent negative reactions coming from families, and how little this changes over longer periods of time. And there seems to be little difference in the way the news is broken.

One of the primary concerns in the aftermath of a disclosure is how the neighbour's are likely to react. This kind of disclosure is perceived to bring great stigma upon a whole family, even where there is little or no evidence of this. Many relatives and friends will claim to be embarrassed, even when there is no reason to be. Friends are embarrassed to be seen with a friend who is going through transition and to be associated with someone who is seen as a freak. This is especially true in those cases where the person transitioning is less than convincing and therefore does not pass well in their new social gender role. It is highly regrettable that families, friends and work colleagues can be so shallow and superficial, but unfortunately that is too often the reality for most of those transitioning towards complete gender reassignment. It is at times like these that each individual must remember the reasons for being in that situation in the first place: that they were diagnosed with a congenital and neurobiological condition, for which they are in no way responsible, despite how others might make them feel.

It is entirely understandable that families should feel shocked, dismayed and confused about receiving the news that a loved one is of the opposite gender to the one they have known all their lives. It is absolutely appropriate that families and friends be given time to absorb and come to terms with such life changing news and to develop the appropriate response to it. It is of the utmost importance therefore that families be given as much accurate information and support as possible. It is absolutely vital that the initial stages of the disclosure process be handled with the utmost sensitivity. Accuracy of information is *everything* in this situation, as is the manner in which it is presented.

The person making the disclosure is normally completely alone when telling their family and friends and is rarely in a position to cope with the various reactions expressed by those around them. Reactions can be anything from very positive and supportive to an immediate break-up of marriages, families and friendships; with the GID person left entirely alone to pick up the pieces. It's no wonder then that many of those making a disclosure opt for a more defensive way of approaching the situation. They will have already heard of the number of negative reactions that others have received and the resulting fallout, so they opt for going in with all guns blazing and insist that their families and friends accept them in their new situation, whether they like it nor not. It can be no surprise to find that this approach *never* works and most likely never will.

In the workplace these individuals can suddenly find they are isolated from their work colleagues and open to bullying, harassment and even losing or giving up their jobs (being forced out through bullying and discrimination). For some self-employed people it can mean the loss of clients who are unwilling to continue giving business to a person living within their changed gender role, despite the fact that there is no deterioration in their work or services. Thankfully there are employers and clients who have demonstrated more enlightened attitudes and have been very supportive of the person making the transition. People going through GID and who enjoy the support of their employers often make for more productive employees and are more loyal to their employers. This fact is often lost amidst the muck that is often raked up against these individuals.

In order to be accepted by their families, some of those making their disclosure will try to reach certain compromises, especially in relation to attending social functions. Consultants rightly frown upon patients changing back to their original gender role when attending special family functions etc. We often hear stories of those who have been invited to various family and other social functions, but on the condition that they change their gender roles back, so as not to make others present feel awkward and uncomfortable. These conditions are laid down regardless of the fact that some have already developed breasts, have a very feminine voice, facial features and mannerisms.

Families are also known to show a complete disregard for how difficult, if not impossible, it is for some individuals to give up their new social gender role and to revert back. This condition is often insisted upon, regardless of the distress it causes and despite the fact that they (the family) had been fully informed of the individual's situation. Needless to say many understandably choose not to attend these social events. This has the effect of isolating them even further and can be used by families and friends as an excuse to distance themselves, while at the same time blaming the person concerned, because they won't see things from the others point of view and won't take their feelings in account.

It is regrettable that, the overwhelming reaction to a disclosure of GID is negative, rarely based on fact and nearly always reacted to in the most acrimonious manner. One of the particularly nasty aspects of people talking about those who disclose their condition is the willingness to go to the lowest common denominator in terms of accusing them of going through a sex change in order to live a sexually promiscuous lifestyle. Or making the rudest and filthy remarks about them and making them the butt of their jokes. These are scurrilous, hurtful and deeply damaging accusations (not to mention slanderous) to people with GID. Without a shadow of doubt, this serves to reinforce much of the misperceptions amongst the general public.

Whatever shock there may be; whatever emotional and legal difficulties there may be, there can never be any excuse or justification for the out and out abuse, harassment, bullying, discrimination and rejection that is meted out by so many families, friends, work colleagues, schoolmates, public service providers etc.

There has been a vulgar haste in the way some spouses

have walked away from their relationships and the levels of abandonment from other family members and friends is quite staggering. This is not helped by the way those with GID mishandle these situations. However, such are the feelings of desperation and the need for self-preservation, that come across as self-obsessed and attention seeking; indeed many people with GID can come across as being selfish and careless of other people's feelings but the majority want to keep their families and their old lives intact. This may be considered unrealistic under the circumstances, but it is their aspiration nonetheless.

One of the other disturbing and damaging phenomena to occur is the advice given to spouses from family and friends to have *nothing* to do with the person making the disclosure. What is also disturbing in this regard is the number of GP's and counsellors who have also given their patients this kind of advice, without any regard for the other person's situation. This advice comes from people who know little or nothing about Gender Identity Disorder or of the true intentions of those diagnosed with it. They epitomise the saying that *a little knowledge is a dangerous thing*. In these types of cases it is very dangerous advice to be doling out. It is very difficult to describe how devastating it feels to be the subject of this kind of behaviour and how powerless people feel to do anything about it, especially when it comes from those who once professed love and friendship.

Seeing it from Everyone Else's Point of View

As already mentioned, the reactions of families, friends, work colleagues etc. are all too familiar and for the most part tend to be quite negative. It is like running a gauntlet in order to survive the negative onslaught which most often follows a disclosure. There are extraordinary pressures placed on people with GID to *understand how others feel*; that they should see their *condition* from everyone else's point of view, yet not expect this to be reciprocated. This often includes the use of emotional blackmail and guilt trips. The typical comments are:

"You have to understand how we feel."

"You have to give it time."

"You are not a girl. I had you as a boy and I will never accept you as a girl."

"You are not a boy. I had you as a girl and I will never accept you as a boy."

"You can't tell mum and dad, they'll have a heart attack and it'll be your fault."

"You can't tell mum and dad, they'll get cancer and you'll be responsible."

"You can't tell mum and dad, they'll die and you'll be to blame."

"O god! What are the neighbours going to think?"

"You're bringing shame and embarrassment on the whole family. Do you want to be responsible for that?"

"How could you do that to us?"

"Why are you being so selfish?"

"Think of the children."

"It's just another one of your phases."

"You're just looking for attention."

"Would you ever get lost, you freak."

But what about the feelings of those who have to live with this condition? What about their need for understanding? What about their fears, vulnerabilities, terrors, unhappiness, depression etc? What about the grief they experience at their own personal loss? What about the loss of their own lives; being denied the opportunity to live within their true gender? What about the effects from running the daily gauntlet of other people's cruelty, blame, shame, false accusations, ridicule, prejudice, stigma and discrimination? It is hard to think of another congenital that attracts so much of society's misunderstanding and stigma.

This is a point that is too easily lost amidst the highly emotionally charged atmosphere that surrounds any disclosure of Gender Identity Disorder. And it is precisely for this reason that we should seek the earliest possible diagnosis now and for those children coming along in the future generations. It is by having the earlier diagnosis that we can avoid these types of traumatic situations from arising in the future. This generation can do much to prevent future generations from being condemned to the same fate.

The Implications for Families

As already mentioned, there are also real and legitimate concerns for families whose loved ones undertake Gender Reassignment. It is unfortunately true that in the majority of cases where a disclosure of GID is made within families, that such disclosures tend to be handled very badly indeed and in some cases with disastrous consequences. For starters, there is the issue of how the spouse or partner can reconcile being married to someone of the same gender (sex), especially when this was not what they signed up for when they entered into the marriage or partnership. These spouses and partners are entitled to feel hurt and let down under these circumstances, which have turned their lives completely upside down. Those who find themselves in this situation are expected to live in same sex relationships when they are in fact entirely heterosexual. There is also a tremendous impact on the lives of children, whose mother or father changes gender, thus leaving them with two parents of the same gender. Spouses and children of People with GID are entitled to feel disturbed as they struggle to come to terms with the consequences for them when their loved one changes his or her gender and legal identity. And where there is a question over the legal status of their relationship to the person undergoing gender reassignment. It is quite unrealistic and indeed unfair to expect them not to be concerned, nor to fight to protect what for some is the only relationship they have ever known. A relationship that is threatened is bound to have deep emotional, physical, financial and social consequences. It is a perfectly normal human reaction. There is no easy way of resolving this kind of situation other than to get through it with the greatest sensitivity and dignity possible. It is at this point that both parties are in need of appropriate professional assistance as they struggle to navigate their way through this unchartered territory.

Apart from people with GID being treated as pariah, others can testify to being subjected to blame for all manner of things that have nothing whatever to do with them. In one case the excuse made for not being supportive was that the person in question was afraid that their children would be bullied at school; even though these children lived in a completely different part of the country! This is typical of the nonsense that people will come out with in an attempt to hide their own discomfort and prejudice. How on earth people make such nonsensical leaps of the imagination is quite beyond comprehension, but people will grasp at even the weakest straws in order to justify their own negative attitudes. The effect is always the same, the further isolation of the person disclosing their condition.

Some can state with justification that it doesn't matter in the least how correct the approach may be in making a disclosure, or, how much understanding and patience is demonstrated in allowing people time to come to terms with the news. There is still an unacceptably high level of rejection and abuse from amongst family, friends and work colleagues. Even the most basic human decency can be missing from those once considered to be their nearest and dearest. It should be no surprise then that so many feel they have no option to but to go it alone, and withdraw and live on the fringes of society. There is no escaping the reality that these situations arise, because loved ones are often more concerned about hiding their embarrassment and shame at having one of their own family with this condition.

The Children of GID Parents

We must never under-estimate the problems for children whose parent's are undergoing a change in gender role. They can be very great indeed, especially for older children who are more sensitive to the opinions of their peers etc. There is also the perceived risk of losing a very precious relationship with a much loved parent. There is also the loss of the father or mother role model, especially for young boys whose father is now living as a woman and vice-versa. There is a real disorientation and distress for children whose parent's change gender roles.

It will come as something of a surprise to many to know that a significant number of children manage to cope well with the parents change in gender role. This is because of the careful and sensitive way *both* parents work together in the best interests of the children. This is not for a moment to suggest that these children will not be affected in some way; but having loving parents who really do care and who put their children at the centre of the situation do tend to fair much better than where there is none or poor communication and poor cooperation between the parents.

Apart from how changing gender roles can greatly exacerbate existing marital tensions, there are also cases in which the non-GID spouse would use their children as pawns and seek to prevent the GID spouse from having access to them; regardless of how well the children may be adapting to their parent's changing gender role. The spouse who uses children in this way is often aided and abetted by other family members, friends etc. It is nearly always done on the pretext of what is in the best interest of the children. This is done even in cases where there is not a shred of evidence that the children are in any way at risk or adversely affected by a parent changing gender role. This is especially true in cases where the change of gender role is being well managed and where the children's needs are given priority.

More often than not it is other adults who are transferring their own fears and prejudices onto the children and in so doing fail to come to terms with the new situation. Thankfully the courts in this country, along with social services, take this into consideration where legal separation and divorce is an issue.

While it is entirely understandable on the one hand, that the spouses and children of those with GID do not wish to share the stigma that goes with the person's decision to change gender roles, neither should they have the right to reinforce that same stigma towards those loved ones who have made a perfectly legitimate decision to change gender roles. This is important given that such individuals are acting upon a prescribed treatment path, from competent experts in the fields of psychology, psychiatry and endocrinology.

This then is the background against which people with GID struggle to cope and against which a decision has to be made on whether to continue with the gender reassignment process. It should be remembered at all times, that no matter how much a person with GID may long to live in their true gender; any decision to go forward for gender reassignment is an indescribably difficult one to make. However once the diagnosis is received there is really no going back, regardless of the enormous difficulties there are in going forward.

There really are no easy answers for those families confronted with this awful predicament, which is why it is imperative that we all learn about this condition at the earliest possible opportunity and thereby prevent these situations from arising in the first place. It will mean that future generations of children born with Gender Identity Disorder will be spared the very problems and life crises which are now being experienced by so many. If this book helps towards achieving this vision then it will have all been worthwhile.

Legal Implications for Families

It should be clear by now that the position taken throughout this book is one of respect for those struggling with their GID and those who are inevitably affected by its impact upon their lives and relationships. It is far from an easy thing to achieve, but it is however the author's contention, that the rights of those with GID, and who opt to go through gender reassignment, should be protected. However this should not be at the expense of their spouses and children. Equally though, it must also be the case, that as distressing as the situation is for the spouses and children, the rights of people with GID should not be denied either. It does take the Wisdom of Solomon to decide on many of the complex issues involved, but nonetheless, it must be done. As things presently stand, the laws of this country are decidedly in favour of the *status quo* and the retention of the rights of families.

The Irish state does not currently recognise same-sex marriages or civil partnerships, and therefore, couples who are opting to stay together, where the diagnosed spouse opts to change their name by Deed Poll, need to consider their legal options in such an event. There are at least several options for families who need to work through this distressing situation.

Maintaining the Status Quo

The first of these options is to maintain the status quo, i.e. do nothing. This is achievable where the person diagnosed with GID opts *not* to go through full gender reassignment. In such cases a decision may be made, and with the support of the other spouse, to live between the two genders. As this will often involve the diagnosed spouse opting *not* to change their name by Deed Poll; the legal status of their marriage remains unchanged. It may also include a decision for both parties to attend counselling in order to support each other in their decision and to enable them to work through their issues together.

Separation & Divorce

In cases where spouses feel they cannot continue within a marriage involving another with GID, they are perfectly within their rights to opt for judicial separation and divorce. In such circumstances both spouses have access to the same Family Law as applies in other cases involving family breakdown.

It is not for *anyone* to tell, persuade or coerce any spouse into making any decision that is against their own long-term interests. It is difficult enough for any spouse to have to come to terms with a diagnosis of GID and thereby have their entire world turned upside down, without having the added pressure of people trying to influence the hard decisions they must make about their own and their children's futures. It is also worth repeating however, that no matter how hurt or devastated a spouse may be under these extraordinary circumstances, nothing whatsoever can ever justify the *using* of children to get back at a spouse who has opted to go through with full gender reassignment.

Nullity

It is not a widely known fact that Civil Nullity exists within this country. This is because marriage annulment was so long associated with the Roman Catholic Church. Civil Nullity is a possible option and it covers cases involving a diagnosis of Gender Identity Disorder. In cases where a marriage has irretrievably broken down as a consequence of one of the spouses being diagnosed with GID and opts for full gender reassignment, then Civil Nullity may be an option. However this option needs to be given very careful consideration where there are children involved. The option of Civil Nullity is probably most appropriate in those cases where there are no children and where hereditary rights are not an issue.

Whatever decisions are made in relation to resolving these complex issues, it should always be borne in mind that these situations stem from a clinical diagnosis. This is vitally important in terms of how spouses move forward and how their decisions and behaviours are likely to impact upon themselves and their children and their children's ability to cope with what is bound to be an extraordinarily difficult situation. In any event, it is imperative that all those affected seek the most appropriate support and legal advice available.

There is no doubt that a change in gender role does exacerbate the problems of marriages that are already in difficulty. However in some cases the diagnosis of GID and change in gender role are blamed as the primary cause for the marriage breaking down, when that is actually not the case. This is too readily accepted by the families involved, and it points to the need for a more careful assessment being undertaken when decisions have to be made on how to proceed legally. But regardless of this, there can be no denying that any diagnosis of Gender Identity Disorder is bound to have tragic consequences for all concerned. It does not serve anyone's long-term interests, especially not where children are involved, to engage in mutual recriminations. These situations are best dealt with by spouses, partners and children understanding that as awful as a disclosure of this nature undoubtedly is, it is first and foremost a clinical condition and it is therefore completely unfair and unhelpful to blame the person who has the great misfortune of having to make such a disclosure in the first place.

Chapter Nine

Afterword

Chapter one asked the question: *why do we need to know about Gender Identity Disorder?* I responded by saying that such is the nature of GID and the extraordinary treatment required, that it impacts hugely on the lives of those diagnosed. What makes this condition like no other is the enormity of the changes that must take place in order for these people to live anything like a normal life. How many conditions do we know of that literally requires a person born in one gender to begin living in another; to quite literally turn their lives inside out?

It is sometimes hard to believe that we are living in the third millennium AD and *not* the third millennium BC, given the extraordinarily backward attitudes we still have toward anyone or anything that is different or perceived to be outside of the *norm*. There is, regrettably, nothing new in this and history is full of so many examples of the price people are made to pay for *being different* or daring to think outside of the norm. For example, there was a time when people like Christopher Columbus could have been burned at the stake or excommunicated for holding that the earth was not flat as most people of the time believed. Or Galileo, who was silenced for stating that the earth is not the centre of the universe and that the earth rotates around the sun and not the other way round. There have been many myths and superstitions that have prevented the human race from advancing and which cost the human race dearly. They were fearful of anything that was different and that would require them to step outside of their comfort zones. And they were willing to sacrifice the best human qualities in order to remain in their ignorance. We face similar challenges today when we raise questions about the true nature and causes of gender and sex.

Thankfully things have changed in more recent times and we are learning that we have nothing to fear from knowing more about the wonders and complexities of nature. We are learning that sex and gender are not as black and white as was so often believed in times past. We are learning that sex and gender is not actually the same thing and that though they are linked they are also separate and distinct parts of our human makeup. We are learning that we do not *choose* our gender identity, but that we are born with it and that it is fixed by the time we reach 3-4 years of age. And that no matter what parents, school, religion, government, communities, peers etc., do to persuade us to conform to our physical gender, we can never really escape who and what nature designed us to *be*. There is no escaping though the tremendous damage caused by forcing children, teenagers and adults to live contrary to their true nature. So the sooner we all come to terms with the wonder, mystery and complexity that is human nature, and the reality that we are, each one of us, made differently and uniquely, then the better life will be for us all. And rather than this difference being something to fear, we can view it as something to be celebrated.

In closing then it can be observed that for people with Gender Identity Disorder, there is no such thing as a stress free, guilt free, stigma free, or discrimination free transition towards one's true gender. And this certainly explains why so few are willing to disclose their condition. It also helps to explain why so few seek appropriate medical intervention. Unfortunately this is likely to remain the case until society as a whole gets to grips with the reality of Gender Identity Disorder. There also needs to be a broader acceptance that those born with the condition have as much right as those with any other medical condition to seek the most appropriate and most effective form of treatment available. They should be able to do this without fear of ridicule, being unfairly judged, being stigmatised and discriminated against. Only then will we be able to bring out the best of ourselves and each other. Is this being optimistic? Yes, but it is so achievable and so worthwhile.

Chapter Ten

The following stories are published as they were submitted, without any editing, save for grammatical purposes. Each writer has their own unique voice and unique way of describing what it is like to live with Gender Identity Disorder. They are to be commended for both their courage and their honesty in how they tell their stories, and in how they have fought their own very personal battles, for the right to live their lives within their true gender.

Diane's Story

"You Throw Like a Girl"

"You throw like a girl" they said. Yes, even my classmates in junior school could see it, even though I appeared to have the body of a boy. But this was 1950's Wales, I was in a Church School, bullying and psychological abuse were standard fare at the time. Although I was a particularly bright child my education did suffer. I detested school, not because of the lessons, but because of the bullying. I avoided the boys in the yard and hung around with the girls as much as I could. I hated sport, it was always football in the winter and cricket in the summer and I was no good at either. This only drew down criticism from the boys and the teachers and not once was this challenged by anyone because at the end of the day, I was like a girl and girls were not expected to do well in sport.

At eleven I went to the secondary school, the bullying continued, but my learning took off, because now I had excellent teachers, over two years I went up three grades and excelled in the sciences. During this time the bullying did reduce from a certain quarter. Shortly after I started at this school a boy who had tormented me all through junior school had ended up in the same class as me, he got his kicks from pulling and twisting hair, a really vicious character from a big family of thugs. Pulling my hair was the mistake he made. I was always sensitive about my hair which I grew as long as I could, one day when the teacher had been called out of the room for a moment, this boy pulled my hair. That was his first mistake, I told him to let go, he didn't, that was his second mistake. I swung at him from a very bad angle but caught him under the chin, he was so shocked by the fact I'd hit him he let go and fell backwards across the desk, that was his third mistake, this allowed me to punch down at him, the next blow burst his nose like an over ripe tomato. All the pain he had given me over the years was given back to him in full, there and then. I thought I would get in terrible trouble, but I didn't, everyone including the teachers knew this was long overdue - me standing up for myself and this particular bully getting exactly what he deserved.

The one thing that day taught me was that bullying should never be tolerated or facilitated; this still informs my thinking today. Because of that day I became a survivor, with a changed outlook on life, from here on I began to relish life's challenges rather than run away from them. Some Transwomen, in particular, allow themselves to become the victims of the bullies in society, because in their up-side-down reality women are passive beings incapable of assertive actions.

Puberty rolled on with the usual awkwardness one feels, but for me this was the wrong puberty, my body decided to go more masculine on me. The days of having a gender ambiguous body were rapidly coming to an end. It was at this time that sensational stories of 'sex changes' appeared in the press, this made me think that there was something much deeper going on with me. I started reading Jan Morris' book 'Conundrum', I had to sit in the library and read it secretly in a quiet corner, I dare not take the book home. I had very good parents, but the general view of People with GID back then was that we were all deeply mad, I just didn't want to go there with my parents. From finishing 'Conundrum' I was pretty sure that I was "a girl trapped in a boy's body" but what to do? This was my one challenge in life that I just couldn't see a way around, over or under, the gender divide seemed like a social brick wall across my path.

My only option for survival at that time was to become the best damn actor I could and make my way in the world living as a guy. I shot small bore rifle for my club at county level, and joined the local Judo club. After leaving school, I went to college and did a City and Guilds in electronics, this was when I had my first sexual experience with another girl, although enjoyable, it didn't feel right. After 12 months we split up and I wandered for a few years in the wilderness of what we know now to be GID, 'cross-dressing' when I could to keep some sort of grip on reality. It was very much a case of knowing the problem and knowing the solution but how to achieve an outcome. It has to be remembered that even in the liberal and 'permissive' 1970's gender transgression was still treated more like a crime than a congenital medical condition. Getting appropriate medical care was a lottery, most Doctors had no real or valid understanding of GID, most clinicians held very ignorant attitudes toward Transgender people at that time.

I later met another girl, quite by chance in the local swimming pool, who is still with me now, we have been together for over 25 years, proof positive that a relationship can survive - but only if both parties WANT it to. Our love transcends the physical and that is why we have been able to stay together. We had our son to consider too, he was at the centre of my concerns but I need not have worried, he adjusted quickly without any great trauma. It wasn't easy though, we all had to come to terms with the reality that my mind is female, but my body at that time was male. It was soon after we moved to Ireland to escape the rat race to find a better and healthier lifestyle, that time caught up with me. I couldn't keep on acting any more, my partner could see I was in real and very serious trouble; she saved my life by giving me her permission to seek medical help. With this I could get the help I needed, but I didn't just focus on myself in this process. I had to carry my partner and son with me on this journey, I had to make sure they were going to be all right as well, I would finally climb that gender wall, that great obstacle, and get to the right side, trying not to hurt the people I love in the process. Finding the right help was a matter of luck rather than design. However, supportive clinicians and a supportive home environment made for a successful outcome. I was very lucky I had very good medical care, I knew of others who didn't. There followed hormone therapy, electrolysis to remove facial hair and eventually genital surgery to bring my body into alignment with my mind. A four year shamanic journey, finding the true inner 'me' a pathway to self discovery and self understanding. Finally I could put the pain and angst of the past behind me and get on with living. Unlike some Transwomen, I didn't want to be Catherine Zeta Jones, I just wanted to be me, I didn't need to cut my face up to make me more attractive, or acceptable to other people, I am what I am, a middle aged woman trying her best to grow old gracefully. There is nothing unusual about this; I'm just trying to do the same as the majority of other middle aged women I meet in my daily life. It would be very easy to throw money at cosmetic surgery, but then I would cease to be me, it would be a facade. I know who I am now, indeed I always did. Now I can be content and happy with that because my journey has been justly travelled.

I have had a very full life to date, in my late 30's I sorted out my gender anomaly, in my 40's I went back to college, twice, and graduated in Women's Studies and Non-Formal Guidance. Now in my fifth decade of this life, I have taken on a new career, I'm enjoying life and the new challenges that the passage of time inevitably brings. I have made new friends and retained a few old genuine friendships. Had I not made this journey I could not have made living in the male role work. I know this to be an absolute truth and one can only imagine what outcome that might have meant!

Chapter Eleven

Nick's Story

I am a stranger to this country in more than one respect. I am not Irish, I am not catholic or even the least bit religious, I do not consider priests and doctors semi-divine beings, I hate stupidity by choice and wilful ignorance, and I like my dogs on the couch and in my bed instead of on a chain in a muddy backyard. As I said, I am not Irish...

I came to Ireland before I even knew the country to any meaningful extent. My then partner was crazy about greyhounds and since the greyhound industry is bigger only in the US this played an important role in our decision. Later the very subject of greyhound racing, its cruelty and brutality, will open our eyes and offer a glimpse at the real Ireland, the world behind the glossy "Emerald Isle" brochures with their pictures of cute lambs and beautifully clean cows on the greenest of fields. Unfortunately, the disappointment did not stop at the greyhound track. At the time I moved to a small village in County Clare I did not know why I have always been different and never felt at ease with myself or the environment as it perceived me. I thought I was an extreme case of a lesbian because I could not help myself but wear men's clothing, have my hair cut short, do men's work and actually enjoy it, and I have never been attracted to a men in my entire life. Instead I fell in love with almost every one of my better female teachers and a few classmates. Having an intimate relationship with a male person did not enter my mind until my mother, tired of waiting for me to announce the appearance of a boyfriend, asked me whether I was sexually active. I dodged the question somehow and thought about it later. The answer was obviously no, but when I tried to imagine being intimate with a man all I felt was repulsion. This told me that I was a lesbian and I did not really like the thought. I liked guys, I liked being around my male friends, I wanted to be accepted by them, which was unlikely to happen if I was a lesbian. The result was a miserable few years until I met my current wife, fell in love one last time, and accepted things as they were.

The only positive side of our move to Ireland was the house we bought in Broadford, County Clare. Hurdlestown House, built in 1871 on some 3,000 acres of farm and park land all over the Clare Hills, was a dream come true. We only had 96 acres left, but for someone used to measuring land in square meters this seemed like half the country. The house was built in the same style as the famous Dromoland Castle, the Adare Manor, and the like. It had character! However, there were many things it did not have. Although we did have the luxury of a central heating, the water for the heating system came from a solid fuel burner. This meant that I had to get up as early as at 6.00 a.m., get on the 30-years old John Brown tractor without a working back lift, drive out to the timber shed, load one back box with logs of up to 2 meters in length and as thick as a sizeable tree, drive that first load to the garage housing the burner, unload into the burner - all with my bare hands - light that huge beast I could actually walk into, and then repeat the whole thing once more time. I had to do this twice a day to keep us comfortable. With that amount of physical work I dropped a lot of weight and grew even more muscle mass than ever before without any supplements. Living in rural Ireland in the late 1990s there was no need to dress up to go anywhere and I took advantage of that fact running around in heavy work boots and clothes, with the shortest haircut yet, and sometimes even a hint of a "shadow" on my face that came from diesel fumes or some other dirt. I lived my dream! Looking back I think half the population of Broadford did not know for sure whether I was an extreme case of a butch or a funny looking guy after all. I enjoyed this uncertainty.

All finally became clear when I saw a documentary about GID on the German TV we received via the satellite. I was mesmerised when my partner quietly walked in behind me and when the inevitable commercial came she said: "This is what you should do." I did not think for a second before responding: "Yes, you are right. This is what I *will* do." The decision was made and it was a very easy one. I felt liberated and finally at peace with myself the second I spoke those words. I knew there was a road ahead, but I also knew the direction this road would take and where it will finally end.

I did not know where to turn in Ireland. I knew exactly what the treatment entails right down to the initial dose of testosterone cypionate I would need to use and how fast I could increase it. The question was where the support any person with GID needs to start the so-called transition would come from. There was no information whatsoever. I took a risk and approached a GP which turned out to be a big mistake. Today I would have reported him to the Medical Council because of the hostility and undisguised disgust he treated me with. Needless to say, I was not keen on repeating the experience and stayed away from GPs from then on. This episode told me more than I wanted to know about the country I used to adore up to that point and I turned to my doctor colleagues in Germany. It did not take long and a vial with testosterone arrived in the mail together with a prescription from an endocrinologist I used to know. It must sound quite ridiculous, but I almost went to the next mirror to look for facial hair once I withdrew the needle after that memorable first injection. When the first fuzz started to appear on my face, my legs looked more and more like those of a chimp, hair began falling off my head, but wildly growing in places a female does not usually associate with it, I could not have been happier. My voice, which was quite deep to begin with, dropped two octaves within a very short period of time and I realised that I had to tell people I used to know for years who I was when I called them on the telephone. Every time the introduction was met with a stunned silence, a spontaneous "Jeez!" or a cautious "Go away!" I was on cloud nine. I could not help myself and laughed, grinned and told my partner about every single one of these marvellous phone calls.

Even the most wonderful of things has two sides and a transition is not an exception. As soon as I increased the dose to the recommended therapeutic level my skin, back, and shoulders exploded in one of the most severe cases of acne vulgaris I have ever seen and my weight was constantly jumping up and down on the account of fluid retention in all extremities. One of the most drastic changes that affected both my body and psyche equally: I could not stop thinking about sex. I finally understood what genetic men go through while maturing and why they often act out the way they do. It certainly was an exciting time and taught me even more self-control.

I did not realise it, but my wife later described the initial period as a "fantasy play which never ended." She told me I was moody, with periods of euphoria and depression changing like in a rapid cycle bipolar and at times even irrational. In other words, very similar to puberty but with the usual five or so years rolled into a few months. I went through a very difficult emotional time and I dragged those close to me through the same hell without realising it. As my wife later wrote: "I could not really understand what a GID sufferer had to go through. I tried very hard, but between the everyday chores and problems I was like in a daze floating in and out of the two worlds, while our dogs seemed to be the only aspect of both our lives keeping us sane."

At this point I would like to emphasise that my example as described here should not be followed as far as my approach to treatment is concerned. I have never been formally diagnosed. In any other country with an established protocol I would have followed the applicable rules and went for the psychological and psychiatric assessments. I would have done so, even though there was never any doubt in my mind that I was doing the right thing, that I have finally found my true self and would never regret anything I was doing or was about to do. I would advise anyone starting on this road to obtain a proper diagnosis and stick to the prescribed regimen, no matter how unnecessary and even humiliating the process may seem. Unfortunately, there are various types of gender and sexual identity disorders (not all are actual disorders, but are perceived as such) and some are similar in their presentation, which could lead to mistakes that are almost impossible to correct. Furthermore, the often self-prescribed hormone treatment can be dangerous if the patient is not properly monitored. Various types of cancer, deep vein thrombosis, liver damage, osteoporosis, and other serious health problems could be the result of self-medicating. In male GID patients hypogonadism and the atrophy of penile and testicular tissue could lead to a sometimes severe shortage of tissue that is needed to create a neo-vagina resulting in its inappropriately small size or weakness of its walls making penetrative sexual intercourse difficult or even impossible. This warning is especially important for the Republic of Ireland where healthcare is still in the dark ages and is unable to provide the complex medical attention a GID patient requires for a full and successful recovery. There is still only one team working out of Dublin and the service is unacceptable by any measure, but it is better than nothing. Compared with over ten years ago there is a clearly identifiable protocol that can and should be followed. There is still only one team in place and the service is basically unacceptable, but it is better than nothing. My first encounter with the Irish healthcare system, its hostility, humiliation, and degrading treatment, as a GID patient was what drove me to begin the mostly self-prescribed and self-administered hormone treatment. However, owing to my professional and educational background, I knew what I was doing. I was aware of the risks and what tests to request from time to time and under what pretences. I also had a reliable source of medication and it was not the Internet, which cannot be trusted.

After almost 12 months of hormone treatment the time came for me to start thinking about surgery. Due to my immigration status I could not travel abroad and tried my luck at the Bon Secours private hospital in Galway, where I saw a plastic surgeon about a bilateral mastectomy, the first surgical step on the way to the body I was mistakenly denied by nature. Having tasted life as it should have been from the start I longed for more, for the complete experience, the cure.

Once again, the attempt turned out in a disaster. The surgeon, a woman lacking even the most basic human compassion, was inexperienced, incompetent, sounded and acted without confidence but excelled in the art of "passing the buck". She did not make any decision stressing the need to present the "case" to the ethics committee, for I was asking her to remove perfectly healthy organs "without a valid cause". She never did. I was so shaken and upset when I left that obnoxious woman's office that I swore to myself it was all or nothing from now on. There was no way I would even try to see an Irish psychologist or psychiatrist and wrote my own "psychological assessments" any clinic performing gender reassignment surgery requires. A psychiatric rotation finally paid off and the German clinic never doubted those assessments complete with references to the appropriate manuals and other terminology. I am not proud of that and I certainly would not recommend this route to anyone. My only defence is that due to a complete absence of any information on GID in Ireland at that time I felt I had no choice. Looking back I can honestly say that this justification works even in hindsight. The circumstances the Irish society creates for its citizens and, to an even higher degree, its non-citizen residents very often drives them to acts of desperation, especially if these people act differently from what is deemed normal.

Compared to many other GID sufferers I was lucky in many ways, but especially in terms of being able to pay for the surgery I needed. I was not prepared to wait years or even decades for what was a matter or urgency and so I have eventually found the then obscure clinic providing private cosmetic surgery without asking many questions, but for at least two large cheques. The result was appalling, nothing I could have displayed anywhere, but I was not about to pay them even more for corrections and this turned out to be a wise decision because the German/Swiss team in a private clinic in Brandenburg near Berlin did a marvellous job without charging me an extra dime. Dr Daverio's technique is truly unique and produces excellent results which are far better than anything I have seen coming out of any other medical establishment worldwide. The chest reconstruction is brilliant and the phalloplasty allows me to go to any gym and shower or urinate in the open without feeling the least bit self-conscious and in respect of the other function a phallus is expected to perform, my never desperate (house-)wife would be happy to fill in anyone with legitimate interest.

Shortly after the so-called transition was completed, my then partner, Sybille, and I got married in a simple civil ceremony in Limerick. This was a wonderful day despite my mother's tears and my absence from the party for almost four hours while I sat an exam in Constitutional Law at the University of Limerick I was attending at the time. As always, we could not do anything "normally", but life was beautiful and we had high hopes for the future. What could go wrong? We were finally a "normal" couple, lawfully married, reasonably healthy and wealthy, educated and, above all, we had each other. I am sorry to say that Ireland managed to ruin all of that.

I was born in Moscow, grew up in New York, Hamburg, Cologne, and many other places, but I still hold a Russian passport, which is more like a "Do Not Enter" sign than a travel document. It is red, just like an Irish passport, but anyone holding it could as well be painted green and have a huge head with almond-shaped eyes like those creatures in the X-Files. We are even called aliens, are subject to the Alien Act 1935 (as amended by countless subsequent acts), and thus not really human beings. Humanity invented passports, borders, immigration laws, work permits, and so on as a more subtle replacement for the embarrassing, but more honest open slavery. We thought I would not be subject to this kind of treatment thanks to the EU Directive granting all EU citizens the right to work and live in any EU country without any restrictions and have their non-EU spouses join them in those countries. We have applied for a residence permit for me on that basis, which I was actually granted. Unfortunately, an overcommitted and narrow-minded member of the Garda, enthusiastically assisted by an equally biased immigration officer at the Department of Justice felt our union offended their sense of right and wrong and the permit was revoked because the same state that married us refused to recognise this marriage as valid arguing we were still a "same-sex couple" and thus had no rights. We refused to accept this illegal and immoral nonsense and applied for Judicial Review by the High Court. These proceedings took almost three years, cost us €50,000, and ended in an unsatisfactory settlement because the Irish barristers let us down too.

I wish I could summon my initial love for this country back somehow. I loved hurling, I spoke with a distinct East Clare accent on purpose, I loved my sheep, my land, my JCB; I even loved that solid fuel burner and the ancient John Brown with the broken back lift. I do not like myself for seeing Ireland only as a large green prison, but I cannot change the way I feel no matter how hard I try. What my wife wants the most is to cross the Irish border one last time and leave this island forever. I can barely stand being here. Sadly, the kind of alien I am cannot even fly away on a normal airplane, let alone a spacecraft and ironically, the state that does not want a GID-infected alien on its territory is also the one that holds the key to my freedom.

Chapter Twelve

Sarah's Story

I was diagnosed with Gender Identity Disorder (GID) on the 22nd February 2000 and on the 6th July 2000 I commenced hormone treatment called Premarin Conjugated Oestrogens by a consultant psychiatrist, Dr. O'Donoghue. On the 12th September 2005 I changed my name by Deed Poll and also changed all my legal documentation to my new name and identity and all that's left is to undergo gender reassignment surgery to have the male genitalia reconstructed into a female genitalia, which I hope to undergo over in the United Kingdom within the near future.

Before I was diagnosed of suffering with Gender Identity Disorder, I lived a horrible life where I suffered from suicidal thoughts, severe panic attacks, depression and a nervous breakdown. It also didn't help being born into a family of all boys and knowing I was born female but having to live as a male was almost impossible. I started primary school at the age of four and left secondary school at the age of seventeen but because of the way I felt growing up feeling different in relation to my gender I learned nothing in fact. It's only when I reached the age of 26 years old when I began to learn to read and write in my life.

I always knew from an early age I was born female even though I was born physically male. My first memory in life that I can recall was when I experienced feeling different from other boys; I was around the age of five years old, but at that age I had no understanding of life itself so it never bothered me. After I left secondary school I went to live with my grandmother because as a child growing up I spent a lot of my time with her and also felt that to live with my grandmother would give me the freedom to live my own life without having to hide my feelings or to be embarrassed or even humiliated as to be seen dressing as a girl in front of my family. At the age of nineteen is when I experienced for the first time ever in my life a nervous breakdown, which lasted well over a year, which then led to severe panic attacks, depression and feeling suicidal. By the time I reached 25 my health had deteriorated rapidly to where I felt the urge to commit suicide.

The first time I attempted suicide I really didn't know what to expect; all I knew was that I had enough of life and didn't want to continue suffering, so one night while my grandmother was in bed asleep I placed my head into the gas oven and switched on the gas, the first breath I felt nothing, no smell nor fumes, but when I inhaled the second breath something strange happened. For a split second a thought ran through my mind which was of my grandmother and leaving her behind and it was this thought that frightened and stopped me from continuing. The bond my grandmother and I had between one another was the most powerful and loving friendship that two people could share with one another. My grandmother was more than just a grandmother to me, she was a mother and close friend and was always there when I needed someone and stuck by me no matter what life threw at me.

A few days later, after trying to commit suicide, I went to see my general practitioner and after speaking to him in relation to my gender and my feelings of suicide, I was placed on anti-depression medication and was also referred to St. Brendan's Hospital to undergo an assessment towards my gender identity by a clinical psychologist, while waiting to be seen by a gender specialist. Then on the 22nd February 2000, I finally got to see the gender specialist and three months later I commenced on hormone medication called Premarin Conjugated Oestrogens, which I'll be taking until I undergo gender reassignment surgery.

Within a year of taking the hormone medication my life completely changed. I became stronger within myself and although I still suffer from depression and suicidal thoughts, it's not as bad as before being diagnosed with Gender Identity Disorder or being treated with the hormonal medication. In relation to how my family feel about my gender, particularly after spending half of my life living with them and them treating me as their son and now coming to terms with me being their daughter and sister is not as difficult in relation to other people that suffer from the same medical condition and having to cope with their families disowning them because of their gender. But in saying this, it's not easy either; for although my mother now addresses me by my female name she sometimes still refers to me as *he* or *him* particularly in front of both family and friends. And as for my brothers, well I have no problem with them, they all respect me for who I am, but I do have problems with my father, because he won't accept anything and as far as he's concerned I was born his son and he will always treat and address me as his son, which has now led me to completely distance myself from him in all future communications, which to me is very heartbreaking, because my father is a soft and gentle man who has always been there for all of us, and will continue to do so. In relation to speaking to other family members as in uncles and aunts, well there's no need to because I have never seen or spoken to them ever since the death of my grandmother, who sadly passed away on the 17th January 2006, which was a total loss to me.

I now live on my own in a one bedroom county council flat on the north inner city of Dublin which was once owned by my grandmother for when she was alive she was the tenant and after she passed away I became the tenant. It is known to be the worst place in Dublin for anti-social behaviour, joy riding and a magnet for teenage gangs to hang out, because of its open spaces. For almost all of my life while living in this estate, I have been beaten and jeered at because I kept to myself and wasn't seen to mix or hang out with the scum that uses the area. I have tried to transfer out of the area, but because of where I'm living it is very difficult to do so, and the reason for this is if I surrender my key back to the council no other private authority will re-house me because I voluntarily gave up my key. And trying to ask the council to re-house me elsewhere is almost impossible, which is leaving me with two other options and that is that I either become homeless or, continue to remain in this racist and hostile environment.

I have spoken to other people who suffer with Gender Identity Disorder and they say that most working class people are worse than all other people on how they treat people that were diagnosed with the condition or are going through their transition. But from where I'm living, I really don't believe this to be the case, for most of the population of people and particularly the gangs that hang around the area where I live are very aggressive towards me because of my gender. I know many people from both sides of society outside of where I live, particularly those who are well off and those who live in poverty and they are very understanding people, and most people who understand the nature of the condition and know the facts are more at ease with people who suffer from Gender Identity Disorder, because they don't find themselves threatened by us. But there are people in society no matter where we live whether they are educated or not, who continue to hassle people in any way they can whether they are well off or live in poverty; be heterosexual, or homosexual, or be born with Gender Identity Disorder. And the reason for this I believe is that people truly believe that people in society are either born male or female. But in the real world what people don't realise or take into consideration is that sometimes Mother Nature makes mistakes and a person can be born with the physical body of a male but the brain of a female and vice versa, or in some rare cases people are born with both the male and female genitalia and it's this that I believe causes some to retaliate against people with Gender Identity Disorder by calling them freaks or abnormal people.

It's like every day we hear people saying it's great to be normal. Well my question is what is normal and what does normal feel like? Because as far as I'm concerned, there is no such thing as being normal. A person wakes up one morning and says it's great to be normal and then during their day they see a person who suffers from Gender Identity Disorder walking down the street and without any reason use offensive language for the way they look. But it's only when they themselves' have an accident which ends up leaving them disfigured for life that they realise what it feels like to be classed as being a freak or an abnormal person, which is sad to think that society is like this particularly in this day and age. But out of all this there is two things that really upsets and frightens me more than anything else in life, and that's where people, apart from using offensive language towards people who suffer from Gender Identity Disorder, is that they threaten or use violence as well.

Nobody knows what a person that suffers with Gender Identity Disorder has to go through in life; of having to come through life from the day they were born having to be treated as the opposite sex to who they are; of having to humiliate themselves in society; of having to face the fear of being beaten up, raped or murdered, because society treats them as abnormal people; of having to suffer with suicidal thoughts, severe panic attacks, depression and nervous breakdowns, of not being wanted in society, and to have no legal rights whatsoever.

Then on top of that to have to go through years of being medically examined by the medical profession to show that they are 100% genuine. Also people suffering with Gender Identity Disorder can't have any type of relationship with a male or female because the Irish government refuses to allow them to marry one another like other Irish citizens, and those who are married have to get divorced from their loved ones which is totally ridiculous and discrimination. If someone loves another person and is totally devoted to them for life, whether they be heterosexual, homosexual, or be born with Gender Identity Disorder, who gives the church and the Irish government the right to state that this is against the law?

In the Bible it states that two heterosexual people of the opposite sex can marry one another, also two heterosexual people who are first cousins who are of the same family and blood can also marry legally. So I would love someone to point out where it says in the Bible where it's against the law to fall in love and marry someone if you suffer with Gender Identity Disorder. And I know people will be saying that two homosexuals can't marry one another but people who suffer from Gender Identity Disorder are not homosexuals? Because most persons that suffer with Gender Identity Disorder were married and some have children, two homosexuals as in two men or two women cannot have sexual intercourse with one another and give birth, and for a woman who states that she is lesbian and has given birth to a child then she is not lesbian, but bisexual and that's a different story.

And to make matters worse there are no laws in Ireland to protect people's rights that suffer with Gender Identity Disorder and whether they are going or are finished their reassignment surgery. And where they have broken the law for any reason, whether they be male to female or vice versa, will not be sentenced to the prison of their new gender but will be sentenced to a prison of their birth gender, which means that a male to female who underwent reassignment surgery to where they had the male genitalia surgically reconstructed in to the female genitalia, will end up in a male prison with other male inmates, even though she has a female body and female genitalia.

Just imagine your daughter or son grows up to be diagnosed with Gender Identity Disorder and is then sentenced to the opposite prison of their gender identity for breaking the law for some reason or other, and as a parent to know the child you gave birth to is open to be raped, gang raped, or even murdered in an Irish prison and yet the Irish government turns a blind eye to this because they refuse to recognise a person who has changed their name and documentation legally to show their new gender and is either going through or has finished their gender reassignment surgery?

Until the Irish government changes the law to recognise

people in Ireland who suffer with Gender Identity Disorder and have their gender identity stated on their birth cert, people all over Ireland who suffer with Gender Identity Disorder will continue to live through abuse and discrimination and have all their rights violated to the highest degree within society, and this will leave them open to be treated differently from all other Irish citizens.

Now people will be saying that the reason why the Irish government refused to change the birth cert is because if they where to do so it would affect the children in many ways. Well if this is so, then tell me why I'm being targeted with the same technicality as a single person who is not married and never was and do not have children and never will and therefore changing my birth cert won't affect any children?

And as for myself to have my birth cert changed to identify my new identity; I really don't see this ever happening in the near or distant future, so until someone in the government changes the law in this country, I am also left having all my rights violated to the highest degree and to be discriminated against as well as everybody else that suffers with Gender Identity Disorder.

The end

Chapter Thirteen

Sara-Jane's Story

How would I describe what it is like to live with Gender Identity Disorder? To live in the wrong body and live as the wrong gender? Living with GID is like being in a catatonic state. People see a body that looks and acts as though it were dead; that is what happens when you are in a catatonic state; people think you are dead and why wouldn't they? You look for all the world like you are dead. Your body is lifeless and ready for burial or cremation. But all the while you are fully conscious of everything and everyone around you. You can hear them talking about you, whether for good or ill, but you cannot reply. You hear and see their grief, but are utterly incapable of responding, nor can you signal because you are unable to move. All you can do is feel the terror as you watch them lift you into the coffin and prepare to close the lid for the last time; getting ready to bury you. And all the while you have no voice; no way of shouting or of crying; no way to explain the terror of your predicament; no way of explaining to them the true nature of your situation, of the terrible and helpless condition in which you find yourself. To them you are dead. You know that you are not what you seem, but you can't tell them, you can't explain. You so want to explain but you can't. You can't tell them that you are alive and that it's your body that's not working. You try to scream; you try to shout, but all to no avail. No one is listening anyway, and why would they when they don't expect the dead to speak? As the terror of what is coming overwhelms you, you start to cry. Crying is the one thing you are able to do, the only thing, but will anyone see your tears before its too late? And if they do, will they just explain it away rather than face the horror of realising that you are alive; trapped in a seemingly lifeless body, but definitely alive?

Suddenly someone notices your tears and cries out *"she's crying! She's still alive! There's the slightest flicker in her eyes from crying but she really is alive! We must save her; we must not allow her to be buried alive!* And so you are saved.

This is what it is like to be born with GID; to be born into the wrong body and with the wrong gender identity. People think they know what you are but they are wrong, but its impossible to explain it to them because you don't really know why yourself; all you know for certain is that you are not what your body says you are; you are the exact opposite to it. But that's not what other people see and how could they?

Nothing is right. Nothing fits and everything is out of place. Nothing makes any sense and I feel completely cut off from my own reality, because my reality is something else and some place else, not here in this body, not here in this assigned gender identity and gender role; not here in this family, this classroom, this job, this relationship, these emotions, these abilities. The list could go on and on, but the point is it just doesn't make sense; nothing makes sense! The only thing worse is that I don't understand it either, until that is someone somewhere explains it to me. But I try the best I can to comply, to fit in, to do what is expected of me, so that I can feel accepted in some way. It isn't working and it is *never* going to work. It has to be fixed, but how can I fix *it* when I don't know quite what *it* is or, what is causing *it*. I don't even know where to go for help or where to get an explanation. And I'm so frightened, especially when I get these out of body experiences; these experiences of being completely detached from myself and the reality that others have imposed upon me. How do I cope with all this when I'm just four years of age?

As if I hadn't enough to contend with I have to suffer them calling me names; telling me I'm a mental retard; remedial, abnormal, I'm left handed and therefore an Anti-Christ! I'm too tall and my teeth protrude. I'm too sensitive for a boy and I'm always looking for attention just like a girl, except that I'm supposed to be a boy. And then there's the beatings; batterings more like; the verbal abuse is shocking but I'm powerless to defend myself and there's no one to defend me; how could there be when it's my own mother and father who are beating me; when it's my mother telling my father that I'm not worth it; that I'm just a bastard; a mistake; the biggest of her twelve mistakes. But I'm only ten. I'm only small and there's no one to love me or protect me. So tell me, how on earth could I possibly tell anyone that all this is happening to *me*; to Sara-Jane?

My breasts are not growing; my periods haven't started and show no signs of ever doing so. I have this horrible *thing* between my legs and I'm so frightened of what it means. I'm growing hair on my face but I don't want to be like those boys and men and have to shave; that's just not normal for me.

I'm expected to ask girls out but I don't know how to; it's just too unnatural. I don't fancy boys, at least not as a boy and anyway they are so rude, so rough and so cruel. I hate the way they speak about other girls. Did I just say other girls? Yes I'm another girl. That's it; I'm another girl, but how, and why? I just don't know.

I love other girls, but I just want to be their friend, but

I'm not allowed because I'm a boy, a shy and incompetent boy. Boys think I'm weird; especially my brothers and they don't want me hanging around with them. They get my mother to send me to the shops so that they can go off without me. And I cry, like a girl; that's what they tell me, that I'm just a big sissy. I don't fit in with boys and I'm not accepted by girls; my mother tells me that she had twelve mistakes and that I was her biggest mistake. And my father thinks that I'm nothing but a stupid and useless fucker!

I don't know what to do or where to go, except to the canal bridge on Kylemore Road and throw myself into the black water below, at least it looks dark this March night. Is there nothing I can do to change this unhappy life? Maybe if I leave home or maybe if I change my name things will get better? No, that doesn't work either. I'm condemned to live with them for now, but it is just so utterly horrible and I feel so helpless. And now they want to know why I took so long to come forward about feeling that I'm a girl in a boy's body!

I thought that when I got married this would all change, but it hasn't; if anything it gets so much worse as my female traits become more acute and more pronounced. It is especially evident during my interactions with other women and they are certainly noticing that I'm not like other men, either in the way I speak or in the way I act towards them. They are querying why I seem to know so much about being a woman? How could I possibly know how a woman feels and why on earth don't I speak the way other men do? I find it impossible to explain, except what I already know and feel, but that isn't very much at all!

When I'm training I try to hide my feminine hand movements and the way I sit with my legs crossed. But people are noticing, especially when I'm showing the ladies how they are not to bend when lifting. They ask me, *is there something you want to tell us?* I laugh it off, but I get the message: no matter how much I try to hide my female traits others still notice and it is just becoming too stressful.

There's no use in trying to commit suicide. It's time to give it up after so many failures; six in all, and anyway I promised myself I wouldn't do it again, that I would find the courage to live and deal with the problem for once and for all. But this means finding the courage to live rather than die and it means finding the courage to seek help. But what if they tell me that I really am a woman? What do I do then? Will I have the courage to tell my family and then go onto the prescribed treatment? Will I be able to go through with Gender Reassignment? I so want to, but will I when the time comes?

Well, the time has come and gone; August 2003 to be exact, though I told my parents in April of the same year, such was my certainty of being a female. It really was undeniable now and I had to do something about it. So I went to see Dr. Kelly and he told me there was no doubt about it, that I am definitely a woman in a man's body. I was on my own when he told me and it was such a pity that others were not there to hear it for themselves. But it was the most amazing and liberating thing to hear. And it was also the scariest, because what do you do when you know what it is? And how do I come to cope with the reality of the drastic and very visible treatment I'm going through and the way it exposes me to all manner of comments and ridicule? But I have to do it despite all these possibilities. I can try and settle for some kind of counselling or therapy, but they will never rewrite or reconfigure my gender identity. They will never make me feel like a man. I'm not a man, I am a woman and that is how I must live now if I am to survive and have a meaningful life. And so I embark on one of the greatest and scariest journeys of my life.

At the time of writing I have entered the last phase of my transition, which includes being injected with anti-androgens and preparing for surgery. I have changed my name by Deed Poll. It's all very exciting and I already feel like a whole person for the first time in my life. I'm so glad that I failed to kill myself, despite all the difficulties I've experienced since my last attempt. It is wonderful to go outside my front door and be the person I was meant to be, even if others laugh and smirk and say nasty things about me. It's still worth it, even though my family's abusive behaviour continues and they behave despicably towards me. I have my friends and my neighbours and they have been so wonderful and encouraging. And I still have my best friend and some of her family. My clients have kept faith with me. I have so little to complain about, so little to make me feel unhappy. Yes, it really has been worth it and I'm alive. I am Sara-Jane!

Chapter Fourteen

Japh's Story

I have included this story as a fulfilment of a promise I made to a very, very brave man who sought my help, along with that of Integrated Ireland in the hopes of coming to Ireland, where ironically enough he thought he would find greater tolerance and acceptance. His name is Japh and his story is all too typical of those who live within closed religiously dominated societies, where there is no understanding of, nor a willingness to learn about the kind of intersex conditions highlighted within this book. From what Japh has revealed it would appear that he was born with Androgen Insensitivity Syndrome and was wrongly assigned as a girl at birth. He refers to having *a minor sexual ambiguity when I was born*. However, as in the case of David Reimer, Japh went on to identify as male and sought to transition towards living in a male body and social gender role.

Life for people like Japh is unbearably cruel and tortuous, and in many cases lives are lost through murder, execution and suicide. These things should be intolerable to any decent civil society, which Japh believed Ireland to be. His view of Ireland as a more tolerant society and a safe place to live should make us more careful in how we view immigrants and asylum seekers who wish to come here to build new lives for themselves. While this is the shortest of the personal stories included here, it is probably the most upsetting of them all.

No changes have been made to this story (apart from editing) and it is published as it was written and sent to me by e-mail. In bringing this story to you I hope you will realise just how enormous the need is for a greater understanding of Gender Identity Disorder and other intersex conditions, and the need there is for a much wider acceptance, and the right of every person to live a normal and happy life.

Dear Sarah,

Thank you so much for your kind response. Thank you so much for the renewed hope you have given me. Thank you. Please do give my contact to whoever you believe is able to help me make it to Ireland. I am willing to communicate with anyone helpful. I am only reluctant to speak with journalists.

I am fine about you including my story in your book as long as we use a pseudo name. At this stage, I feel closer to you and I know that you really want to help me so I have to open up some more and tell you that Japh is my name but one I use for safety purposes. My real name is Jacob (pseudonym), it is the name known by everyone, especially those wanting to make life so unbearable.

It is also the name in my passport and on most of my other identification papers.

Thank you so much Sarah for your assistance. I don't know what the day will be like when I get to Ireland...that will be the most memorable day of my life, and I look forward to it with everything in me.

Many blessings,
Jacob.

Dear Sara,

It has been a great relief to read from you today. I am not only ready to share my situation with you. I am desperate to find a lasting safety solution in Ireland. I am 37 years old and I have a partner and two adopted children, a girl aged 5 and a boy aged 4.

Although I had a minor sexual ambiguity when I was born, it was not "serious" enough to declare me a boy at birth. I was therefore declared a girl and raised as one. It was not until 1993 – at 23 years of age that I got the guts and the opportunity to face a condition I could no longer contain and so while in Nairobi, I started the transition journey. However, I had no guarantees of supervision or even continued consultation, since to do this I would have to keep moving back and forth between Uganda to Kenya, which would be expensive but also dangerous. I have tried to do this over the years but most of the time I have self medicated – with hormones and treatment for other minor ailments that I would get. In reality I classify as transgender (FTM) but to avoid arrests, I have hidden in my doctor's advice to say that I was intersex.

On many occasions, I have been asked to prove through a medical examination that I was neither transgender nor lesbian, and I could not do this. So I have kept moving from place to place and from job to job. Where I didn't voluntarily run away, I was terminated when I refused to take the medical examination. Since 1996, when my story hit the national news, I have been subjected to horrendous treatment and I can no longer stand it. Even if I tried, my life is now in real danger. I have been evicted from residences, I have been verbally abused, I have been sexually assaulted, a family member of a girl I dated once in 2000 set the house we rented on fire as a warning for my girlfriend to abandon the relationship. Right now, I am employed by a Christian organization, the management of which has made it clear that

167

employing me is a favour because I am "crippled". I am being cheated of wages and being told to my face that I have no rights. In addition, demands have come in for my girlfriend to get pregnant and prove that I am a man or else I will be forced to undergo a medical examination to determine why I am unable to impregnate her if indeed I am a man.

Being homosexual, lesbian, and transgender are all crimes here and sexual deviations against the order of nature. They are met with so much hostility by every sector of the general public, and the hostility and persecution is endorsed by the government. In my despair I have tried to seek assistance from the only other transgender I know here towards leaving the country. She is also trying to see how she can assist.

I also contacted Isabel for advice on how to go about it from the side of Ireland. I need a contact there, people that can help me when I get there but also people that can help me while I am still here preparing to leave. I don't know if there are any sponsors for such an undertaking, any lawyer who can perhaps correspond with me on what I need to do. My story is straight forward and known and I have much of the evidence I need although not for all the persecution I have suffered.

I have for a long time nursed the urge to run away but somehow got a ray of hope that maybe we may win the fight for fair treatment and either stayed back or returned from a neighbouring country I would temporarily be hiding from. All of these have been here in Africa.

The reason I am now desperate to come to Ireland is because twice, I have been made to feel like a human being and that was by Irish bosses. Secondly, I am very fluent in English and most of my work experience has been in the English language. I am certain that I will not only be protected by Ireland but I will integrate easily in the community.

Please let me know your thoughts and how you think I can be helped.

Many blessings.

Japh.

Dear Ms. Cromwell,

Thank you so much for the response. I did figure you might be busy because you mentioned you were in the middle of writing a book.

As I mentioned in my earlier mail requesting for your help, I am still praying and hoping for a lasting settlement solution. Besides hiding from the authorities through the use of fictitious names or in most cases, just shying away from all public activities, I am unable to get proper follow up as I transition. I self medicate - I have done this for the past over ten years and as I grow older, it is crucial that I have proper medical monitoring. I also need to settle because I am raising two adopted children.

Because of the situation I am going through, my partner and I are thinking of giving away one of the children because we cannot move from place to place all the time with two small children.

For now, I am thinking of moving to Kenya temporarily as I figure out how to get to Ireland - or perhaps any other safe place. However, this Friday, 21st I am going to be present - for the first time - in a court hearing where Victor Mukasa (another FTM) is suing the government for abuse of her and her partner's rights to privacy when her house was raided by local council officials and the Police, and her partner arrested on allegations that they were lesbians. I want to be in court that day and see how it turns out. I am taking this bold move because as you know, I have grown quite desperate and seeking all avenues to a solution. We are hoping that due to the forthcoming visit of the Queen of England, we will not be arrested. The government may not want to be in the bad records

of the International community at this time - hopefully!!!
Anyways, we will be in court on Friday and I will let you know
how it will go.

Thanks once again. Let me know any information you need from
me to enable you help me in anyway please.

Many blessings,
Japh.

Postscript

I have lost contact with Japh over the past number of months
despite numerous efforts to keep in touch. Nor have I been
able to receive any information from Integrated Ireland, who
was originally dealing with Japh's case. It may well be that
he went to live in Kenya or some other hiding place, or it
may be that he is dead. We simply do not know at this time.
I can only hope he is still alive and that somehow and
somewhere he will get to see that his story was told to the
people of Ireland.

Glossary of Terms

This glossary includes a variety of terms used in relation to Gender Identity Disorder and other gender related conditions. It is not a definitive list, but it does include those which people are most likely to come across in this country when discussing gender related issues.

Terms

Autogynephelia:
Ray Blanchard, Anne Lawrence & J. Michael Bailey use this term for their theory that people with GID are really just gay people who cannot come to terms with their sexual orientation and so fantasise about being females who use gender reassignment as a way to engage in sexual relations with members of the same sex. The theory also includes the idea of men becoming sexually aroused by the image of being a woman.
This term with its accompanying theories remain unproven and are not accepted by the wider psychiatric and psychological professional bodies and should be treated with caution.

Congenital Gender Disablement:
GID is not a disability in the literal meaning of the term. It can however be extremely debilitating on the lives of those born with the condition. GID can definitely lead to mental illness and psychological problems through depression caused by the sufferer's inability to cope with being in a constant state of conflict, but it is not a disability in itself. Also, people with GID may feel even more stigmatised than they already are by referring to the condition as a disability.

171

Drag Kings and Queens
Male and female impersonators, for entertainment purposes.

Gender Variance
This term is very rarely used and is preferred by those who are not comfortable with the term Gender Identity Disorder. This term is also used as a cover term for those who are struggling with some form of gender problem but who may prefer to remain undiagnosed, but also wish to alternate between the two gender roles, but without committing to diagnosis or treatment. This term may also be used by some individuals who self-medicate on hormones and other medications out of a wish to have some physical appearance in the opposite sex.

Genital Realignment Surgery:
This is the correct term for surgery involving changing from one genitalia to another and should not be confused with those who partially change distinguishing features for non-GID reasons.

Sex-Change:
This was the term traditionally used in reference to anyone who changed their genitalia through surgery. The difficulty has been the negative connotations that go with this term and the way in which it trivialises what is a fundamentally serious need for of surgery, which follows on from a medical diagnosis and prescribed treatment process.

Shemales/Shemen:
These terms are rejected for the same reasons as Transexualism. Transsexuals are also more accurately known

as shemales in that it is a choice for some to live between the two genders, at least physically and for the primary purpose of living a particular sexual lifestyle.

Transgenderism/Transexualism:
These are two of the most widely used terms in reference to GID. However they are also used in reference to some forms of sexual orientation and sexual lifestyle. Because of this they are totally inappropriate for the purpose of describing GID. That said a great many people with GID slavishly use these terms on the grounds that everyone else is doing it. That can never be a good enough reason for using terminology that clearly carries the wrong connotations and only adds to the confusion that surrounds the condition and contributes to the stereotyping and stigmatising of those living with the condition.

Some use these terms in reference to what they call the "Third Sex."

Transsexual Syndrome:
This is rejected for the same reasons as above and also because GID is definitely not a syndrome. It is a congenital neurobiological condition.

Transvestitism/Crossdressing:
Under no circumstances should Gender Identity Disorder be likened to either of these terms. Transvestitism/ Crossdressing is listed as a psycho sexual disorder and a form of fetishism. They are intrinsically about lifestyle and overlap with sexual orientation and are therefore wholly inappropriate as terms to be used in reference to GID.

Endnotes

1 **Dr. Cillian De Gascun**: Gender Identity Disorder in Ireland, Irish Medical Journal, May, 2006.

2 Sunday Times: 1: My Life, Window on Life.

3 **Professor Louis J.G. Gooren** Closing Speech to the Council of Europe 23rd Colloquy on European Law, Free University Hospital Amsterdam.

4 Ibid.

5 **Gleitman**: Psychology, 4th Edition, Norton, 1995.

6 Attributed

7 **Gooren**, et al.

8 **Dr. John Money**: Man Boy, Woman Girl, Baltimore: John Hopkins University Press, 1972.

9 **Lynn Conway**: Basic TG/TS/IS Information, www.lynconway.com

10 Ibid.

11 Sunday Times: 1: My Life, Window on Life.

12 **Lynn Conway**, Basic TG/TS/IS Information, www.lynconway.com

13 **William Reiner**, M.D.: *To Be Male or Female—That is the Question*, 151 Arch Pediatr. Adolesc. Med. 225 (1997)].

14 **Gooren, Swaab**, "Sex-Change", Discovery Health Channel, 2004.

15 Ibid.

16 **J.-N. Zhou, M.A. Hofman, L.J. Gooren** and **D.F. Swaab**: A Sex Difference in the Human Brain and its Relation to Transsexuality.

17 **Gooren, Swaab**, "Sex-Change", Discovery Health Channel, 2004.

18 **Murphy D, Murphy M, Grainger R.**: Self-castration, Department of Urology, St James's Hospital, Dublin, Ireland.

19 My Secret Self- A Story of Transgender Children, 20/20, ABC, 2007.

20 Concluding Observation No. 8, United Nations Human Rights Committee, July, 2008.

21 Catholic News Service, Jan-14-2003.

22 LifeSite News.com, a Roman Catholic Website, March 6, 2008.

23 The Christian Institute.

24 Ibid.

Further Reading

There is a real problem accessing information that is readily understood by the general public and I have had to rely very heavily upon the voluntary efforts of numerous online organisations for the information contained within this book. That in no way detracts from the accuracy of the information contained here, but it does serve to highlight the problem even for People with GID to learn as much as possible about their condition.

Becoming Myself: The True Story of Thomas who Became Sara, Sara- Jane Cromwell, Gill & Macmillan, 2008.

Gender Dysphoria: A Treatable Condition within Mainstream Medicine, Sara-Jane Cromwell, Irish Medical Times, 27th March, 2009

Gender Identity Disorder: 4th September 2000, Interview with Prof. Louis Gooren

Harry Benjamin GID Association Standards of Care For Gender Identity Disorders, 6th Version (2001)

Lynn's Story, Lynn Conway, Lynn conway.html

Suffolk Health Authority, May 1994, Press for Change UK.

Transexualism 102 Fact Sheet, FTMA Network 2005

Transexualism: Introduction & General Aspects of Treatment, Prof. Dr. L. Gooren.

Transsexualism: The Current Viewpoint, Press For Change, UK

Transexuality: An Introduction, Gender Trust, UK

Transsexual and Other Disorders of Gender Identity, Ed. Dr. James Barrett, Radcliffe Publishing, 2007

Transsexuals and Sex Reassignment Surgery: An Internal Report Produced by

Trans People in the New NHS, Dr Zoë-Jane Playdon, Co-Chair, Gay and

True Selves, Mildred L. Brown & Chloe Ann Rounsley,

See also:
'Sex Change': Documentaries Series, Discovery Health Channel.

'My Secret Self' -A Story of Transgender Children, 20/20, ABC, 2007.

'Dr Money and the Boy with no Penis', Horizon BBC, 2004.

'Sex-Change Hospital', Living TV.

'Sex Change Soldier', Channel 4.

Further Information:

Gender Identity Disorder Ireland: 021-4638562, info@gidi.ie, www.gidi.ie

Equality Authority, Clonmel Street, Dublin 2, 01-4759473,